+rosebud no.5 – Mystery

709 · 04075 mys

First published in Germany 2004 by Rosebud, Inc.

© Rosebud, Inc. and Die Gestalten Verlag GmbH & Co. KG, Berlin 2004

ISBN 3-89955-037-4

Printed and bound in Germany

Supported by DIESEL

To Our Parents

Welcome to Mysteryland

                                                         –

The land where the boundaries blur
between reality and fantasy.
Where imagination is not limited by
the constraints of a common sense that
seems all too uncommon, but encouraged
to roam freely through a world filled
with unexplored secrets.

A world that is at the same time familiar
and alien, simple and complex,
peaceful and violent, beautiful and ugly,
joyous and sad.

A world in continuous flux.

Can you imagine such a place?

Are you dissatisfied with the familiar overrationalized, scientific and mechanized worldview?

Are you prepared to abandon the common cultural channels and venture into another realm—one that is entirely new and unpredictable?

In Mysteryland we look to the heavens
—once an object of superstition, awe
and fear—but now recognized as a vast
repository of knowledge.

And we look down to mankind. To the
profound and elusive connection that
every human creature has to every other.
To the act of creation and birth. To love,
hate and human emotion, however
unquantifiable, as the most powerful
impetus driving human existence.

In Mysteryland we ask why is something
this way and not another?

But be warned.

Mysteryland is not a safe haven for passive seekers of spiritual enlightenment engaged in a vain pursuit of turning back the hands of time — those who want so desperately to reestablish what they believe to be a simpler and (as they would have you believe) purer lifestyle.

So, should you desire to immigrate to Mysteryland we require that you verify the sincerity of your intentions and quantify the purity of your spirit.

No trespassing by rationalistic positivists will be allowed; and their so-called enlightened community will not be permitted to demystify our fragile world, a world based on the principles of desensualized perception and a higher state of consciousness.

«Welcome to Mysteryland» was recorded on tape and sent out to over 200 prospective contributors worldwide.

Contents

---   –

Fairytales

By Chloë Potter

Of Cats, Quanta and Cephalopods

---   –

By Peter Schattschneider with Illustrations by Timo Reger

---   –

Introduction

This essay was written in 1992. Many things have happened
since then, and then again not. The peculiar laws of quantum
mechanics have been brilliantly confirmed. We can now observe individual atoms in an unreal superposition of neither-here-
nor-there, in so-called «cat states.» Particles of light are apparently teleporting in contradiction of the theory of relativity.
Large molecules are capable of passing through two widely
separated holes simultaneously.[1] The role of the observer has
been relativized, inasmuch as the transition to the classical
mode of observation has more to do with the disappearance of
interference terms in extremely short time spans than with
observing. Nevertheless, quantum mechanics remains enigma-
tic. Today, in a new millennium and a hundred years after its
introduction, we are at least as far from understanding its laws
as we were then. Thus, to the authors' astonishment and de-
light, it was not necessary to make many changes in the text.
The most substantial modification was changing the Austrian
currency to the Euro.

    Is it not amazing that cats have holes in their pelts exactly
where the eyes are, asked Georg Christoph Lichtenberg, an 18th
century physicist, who bequeathed us physics and aphorisms.

Physicists like cats and amazements. There are some cats, claimed
Erwin Schroedinger two centuries later, that are neither alive
nor dear. For a time, Schroedinger adorned the thousand-
Schilling note in Austria. (Mozart was pictured on the ATS 5000
note, which quite precisely reflects the relative value of science
and art in this wondrous country.)

After tuning up here, we will let Schroedinger's cat out of
the bag, and both its grandfather and its children will spring out
as well. First, however, we need to describe the ecology where
this independent creature enjoys its nonexistence.

Quanta — A Hopeless Mess

Around 1900, in the course of research for the booming electric
light industry in Berlin, Max Planck stumbled on a new natural
constant, one that indicated that radiant energy is not emitted
continuously, but rather in packets, in quanta. At this point, it
is well worth remembering that quantified energy clashed
utterly with a physics that, up until that time, had been steady,
homogeneous and smooth. Quanta were like a rap interlude in
Finlandia, or like a cubist period from Rubens. Max Planck did
not like his fudge factor—which he designated «h»—at all.
A general disturbance commenced among physicists, one that
would last nearly 30 years.

Not until 1927 could Werner Heisenberg present a wor-
kable version of «quantum mechanics,» as this theory of the
microcosmic would soon be known. That the theory took 27
years to formulate had little to do with any laziness among first-
team physicists, but rather with quantum mechanics' apparent
contradiction of many notions that had previously been regard-
ed as reasonable. As Max Born, one of its proponents, said,
«Quanta are a hopeless mess.»

An introductory sentence from Heisenberg's original
paper makes clear how deep the cognitive problems raised by
the new theory were. «In this paper, exact definitions of the

following terms will be established: location, speed, energy...»[2]
No wonder that the doubts raised about the fundamentals of
the most exact of all disciplines shook the scientific community to its foundations.

In postmodern physics, this problem would probably be
addressed differently. The words location, speed and energy
would have been left in peace, and instead a probabilistic remote
action would have been postulated. But today theories are cre-
ated differently; information is the message and the main thing
is to publish first.[3] Admittedly, a postmodern quantum mechanics would also have to face the basic problem that Niels Bohr
believed he had disposed of with his «Copenhagen interpretation» of the theory. This approach remains the official philosophical basis for the peculiar formalism of quantum mechanics.
But things tend not to follow official readings. Ordinances can
no more determine collective happiness, truth or reality than
safety regulations can prevent catastrophes in atomic power
plants. In point of fact, the Copenhagen School had only hidden
the basic problem with quantum mechanics so well that it
remained unfound for half a century. This careful camouflage
led renowned scientists to make adventurous statements about
the role of human consciousness in measuring location, speed,
energy and other properties. The physicist Eugene Wigner even
speculated about extrasensory perception.[4]

Schroedinger's cat is also a product of this basic problem, which,
despite assertions to the contrary, can be well understood
without special knowledge of physics. These assertions are very
probably based on the fact that lack of special knowledge about
physics actually makes understanding the problem easier. We
will illustrate it with a simple example that can serve as a pre-
cursor to Schroedinger's cat, and draw on this example to bring
this animal's fantastical story up through 1982.

The Cat's Grandfather

Light is well known as a wave's movement. Waves emanate from a light source as from the point where a stone is thrown into still water. These waves can be reflected, broken, superimposed— all according to the laws of classical wave physics that generations of students have learned through exercises with the «wave pan.» Speaking of water waves rather than light waves, and tossed stones instead of light sources only means that we have a model of light propagation that allows us to study all of the phenomena that interest us in this context, and particularly the aforementioned basic problem of quantum mechanics.

What we do not have yet is an analog to observing the phenomena; light waves are not visible in the way that water waves are. A physicist who wants to investigate optical phenomena places a film, which might also be the light-sensitive cells in the physicist's retina, along the light's path. In our model, we replace the film with a sandy beach that the water waves wash up on. Just as a film turns black from light, the sand shows impressions of where the water has been. Closer examination of the developed film shows that the emulsion is comprised of individual grains of silver bromide. Restricting the intensity of the light source does not mean that each grain will be darkened less, but rather that fewer grains will be darkened at all, as any amateur photographer knows. With a brief enough exposure, just one grain would be exposed. Pre-informed readers know that this exposure results from the single photon emitted by the light source.

Thus we need another analog for photons (things that can darken a grain) in our model. Consider small boats, or perhaps nutshells. Imagine, for a moment, that small nutshells fly off of the thrown stone, get carried along on the wave and, where they reach the shore, leave indentations in the sand. It is important to recognize that the waves could have nothing to do with the darkening, because they would not produce single-point impressions (individual exposed molecules of silver

bromide) but instead would form broad dunes, a phenomenon that has never been observed.

It soon becomes clear that the nutshells have to have peculiar properties. For example, we could build a breakwater outside the harbor with two gaps. The nutshells would no longer reach the shore evenly, but would come in with the same characteristic striped pattern that two overlapping waves would have, what physicists call interference. If one of the gaps were closed, some nutshells would not fail to appear; instead, the ones coming through the other gap would suddenly change course, as if they knew that the first, separate gap had been closed. The piles of nutshells — which of course can only be noticed after enough time has elapsed to allow a sufficiently large number of them to reach the shore — are always where the waves are high.

There are two possible interpretations of this story. First, one can assume that the nutshells are intelligent and know what is happening far away at the moment that it transpires (they would have to be capable of extrasensory perception — ESP), in which case waves are not necessary for the explanation at all. Alternatively, one can retain the concept of waves, which explains the distribution of the nutshells so clearly and correctly, in which case the nutshells are not necessary. In fact, they are first observed on the beach, and never beforehand![5]

We thus face a choice between accepting intelligent nutshells with ESP and assuming that the nutshells first arise on the shore, in precise proportion to the height of the waves. This is a rough dissection of quantum mechanics' basic problem, a point that blatantly contradicts experience. Reason resists both nutshells with ESP and the autogenesis of matter at the crests of the waves. More precisely, at the wave's height, the most peculiar thing about its behavior is that the entire wave train collapses with the appearance of a nutshell. It's as if an entire pond turned over and went completely flat. In terms of the experiment with light waves: as soon as the film absorbs the photon, darkness sets in.

The physicists around Niels Bohr were of the opinion that the second assumption was the lesser evil. This view was shared by both Bohr and Einstein, who seldom agreed. Einstein remarked, «The thought that ... an electron makes a free decision about the moment and direction that it leaps out is unbearable. If that is true, then I would rather be a cobbler, or even a croupier in a casino than a physicist.» We should be grateful that Einstein did not foresee the developments yet to come; he probably would have changed his profession.

But even the lesser evil, which led to today's mainstream interpretation, produced its share of unease. The Copenhagen group around Bohr camouflaged it behind an elegant formalism that exactly described the observations. Their brilliant step was to consider the propagating waves, which seemed to collapse mysteriously when a nutshell appeared, as probabilities. The height of a wave at a particular point corresponds to the probability that a nutshell will appear there. The wave with the strange property of producing nutshells and then collapsing for unknown reasons was thus not real. Instead, it should be conceived as «potentia» or propensity, as Karl Popper said later, as just the possibility that something will happen in a particular place. It was, so to speak, an epistemological con, one that made bearable the idea of a wave that could, after some secret command, collapse suddenly and utterly. This interpretation provided a preliminary explanation for what Erwin Schroedinger had actually found when, in 1926, he discovered his famous wave equations. They worked, but nobody knew what they described. Physicists judged the situation as hopeless, but not serious, as this poetic summary from a colleague of Schroedinger's shows:

Erwin's wave function
is a nice calculation
But we would really like to know
What on earth it's supposed to show.[6]

In the Copenhagen interpretation of quantum mechanical formalism, the probability is the actual physical quantity, given as
a number between zero and one. This number follows the rela-
tively simple Schroedinger equation, and can thus be calculated
precisely in advance. The concept of a probability wave is abstract, but comforting, because it behaves like other waves normally behave. In this case, chance follows a law, in the form of
Schroedinger's equation. If a measurement is taken, in effect
letting the wave hit the beach, then this law-abiding behavior is
disturbed, in fact destroyed. The nutshell materializes somewhere, according to the laws of probability, the wave collapses
and forgets the equation. Observation invalidates the equation.
It appears as if the behavior of waves and nutshells depends on
whether we measure it or not. That is the oft-cited influence of
the observer on the object measured, and it can now be seen
that this apparent influence arises from the choice, made
above, of the lesser evil. If we had instead chosen nutshells with
extrasensory perception, there would have been no «influence
of the observer,» because there would have been no waves that
collapse when the observer looks in.

As problematic as the epistemological justification for
quantum mechanics was, it worked. The new formulas described atomic energy levels, electron orbits, radioactivity and much
more, with exceptional precision, which continues to this day.
Roger Penrose writes, «The theory has two effective arguments
in its favor and only a small one against it. First, through the
present day, the theory corresponds with all experimental
results with an unbelievable degree of precision. Second, it is a
theory of profound mathematical beauty. The only thing that
can be said against it is that it makes no sense at all.»

The part that makes no sense is the ontological problem.
Where are the nutshells, if there is no beach? The Copenhagen
school gives a pragmatic answer: no measurement, no photon.
All that we know anything about are coincidences of space and
time (ticks of an instrument, film exposure in particular places at particular times), and these take place quite precisely

according to the theory of probability waves. The question, «Where is the photon before the measurement?» is as meaning-less as the question, «What was there before time began?»

This extreme view of reality is a radical use of Occam's Razor: *Entia non sunt multiplicanda praeter necessitatem.* Cutting away unnecessary premises was an influence of positivism. In this context, it is natural to think of an analogous development in philosophy that began by eliminating «things in themselves» and finally led to a subjective idealism. (This book disappears when I close my eyes.)

Carried over to our example, this does in fact mean no beach, no nutshell. There is only a distribution of probabilities that col-lapses at the moment of measurement, for example when a sil-ver bromide grain in the film (the measuring instrument) turns black from its encounter with an observed photon.

But now the situation becomes even more peculiar. Does the probability wave collapse at the instant of the film's exposure, or only later when the film is developed? The silver bromide molecules in the emulsion are made of atoms, and these are also probability waves, as quantum mechanics has shown with such great success. So at the moment of exposure, it is not correct to say that the probability wave has collapsed, the observer has to see it first! Ultimately, the laws of quantum theory are also valid for the formation of the image on the retina, and the organic processes in the brain are also atomically regulated, that is, they are also nothing more than superimposed probabilities. Only the observer's consciousness can make something real out of this chain of probability waves. Mathematician John von Neumann proposed this theory of measurement in full posses-sion of his not inconsiderable mental powers. To refresh the memory, a quotation from his paper: «Measurement, and thus the preceding chain of subjective apperceptions tied to the measurement, is a new thing in the physical environment, one that is not ascribable to it. This new thing leads out of the

and offers to adopt Jeff.

physical world, or more accurately it leads inward, into the uncontrollable, mental life of the individual.»[7]

The Cat

Stated plainly, the credo of quantum mechanics is that the observer creates the world. J. A. Wheeler speaks of observation as an «elementary act of creation. In a strange way, the universe is a participatory universe.»

How far this revolutionary point of view runs counter to our understanding of reality was already clear to the Schroedinger's cat's grandfather. In 1935, two things were clear. First, quantum mechanics is an excellent theory, and second, that for the foreseeable future it would be necessary to live with the theory's peculiarities. Schroedinger himself summarized quantum theory's epistemological fundamentals in an essay whose title, «The Current Situation in Quantum Mechanics,» suggests the author's dissatisfaction. (Schroedinger never dreamed that the situation would last through the end of the millennium.) In this essay, to illustrate quantum mechanics' peculiar effects, Schroedinger invented his now-famous cat. As he writes:

«It is, however, possible to construct positively burlesque cases. A cat is locked into a steel chamber, together with a diabolical machine that must be kept away from direct access by the cat. In a Geiger counter's tube is a very small amount of a radioactive substance, so little that in the course of an hour, it is possible that a single atom will decay, but just as likely that no atom will decay. If an atom decays, the counter will register that, and via a relay will move a hammer that destroys a flask containing cyanide gas. If this system is left on its own for an hour, it is possible to say that if no atom has decayed, the cat is alive. The first decay would have led to its poisoning. The psi function [probability wave] of the entire system would express the situation in terms of a living cat and a dead cat ... being equally mixed, or spread across the system.»

Schroedinger's intent is clear: something less daft should be devised.

At this point, the well-disposed reader is likely waiting with great interest for the salvation of the half-dead cat. It's time to let slip that to this day the dog has not been found. In the meantime, however, a number of clues have been found.

The first clue is in our simple pond and nutshell analogy. Recall that when a nutshell appears, the entire wave collapses instantly. That should mean that as soon as a nutshell appears at point A on the shore, an observer on the opposite shore, point B, no longer has a chance of finding a nutshell because the probability wave has collapsed everywhere after the measurement at point A. It appears that the result of an experiment at point A can instantly influence what is possible at point B. This brings the extrasensory perception, which we had hoped to eliminate by denying the existence of nutshells before the measurement, back into the picture. Einstein and two colleagues made this idea more precise in a famous essay from 1935, entitled «Can the Quantum Mechanical Description of Reality Be Considered Complete?» The paper shows that if quantum mechanics is true, the condition of particle B depends on what is observed about particle B, even if these particles are light years apart. For Einstein, this was so obviously impossible that the premises must be false. Bohr's answer, which appeared under the same title, said, essentially that it is correct that the condition of particle B depends on what happens with particle A. However, he went on, it is not a matter of real conditions, but rather of probability waves, of possibilities, and this fact is astonishing but neither contradictory nor paradoxical. Why should something be wrong with quantum mechanics?

The Descendants

It would be 30 years before John Bell found an answer to this question by extending Einstein's thought experiment. He showed first that the results of experiments with particles A and B follow a particular relationship, Bell's inequality, if the experiments on particle A have no effect on the results of experiments on particle B. (This is normally glossed over as common sense: the results of one observer's experiments rolling dice do not influence what another, distant observer rolls. This fact is described as the separability of the world.)[8] Bell then showed that quantum mechanics predicted experimental results that violated the inequality. That proved the following:

Either the world is comprised of individual building blocks and dispersible, as a small child imagines, and quantum mechanics is false, or quantum mechanics is true, and the world is not separable, but much more complex than we had thought, with everything interconnected. The angry tirade of a cephalopod from Alpha Centauri 6 that can only get Dynasty re-runs on its interstellar video connection could directly influence the outcome of an experiment on earth involving a certain cat and a radioactive atom.

The hitch is that in 1965, when Bell discovered the inequality named after him, no one was capable of performing the suggested experiments. They fell short in technical details, such as the generating sufficient quantities of the requisite probability waves, or choosing the right picosecond for measurement. Thus Bell's results offered two fascinating alternatives, but no decision. It was a matter for logicians, aesthetes and mystics. Experimental physicists did not even trouble themselves enough to ignore Bell's work. Until 1982, no one knew whether quantum mechanics was false, or if a fit of extraterrestrial anger could kill a cat. Then Alain Aspect presented experimental results showing that Bell's inequality was false;[9] thus quantum mechanics is correct, and cephalopods from Alpha Centauri 6 can in fact influence our lives.

Why that should be, remains unknown. The development of quantum theory, as described here, brought about new and exciting insights into the microcosmos. However, we still cannot incorporate it into a fully coherent picture of the world. As Richard

Feynman, a Nobel laureate in physics, wrote in 1965, «I think I can
safely say that today nobody understands quantum mechanics.»

Naturally, immediately after Bell's publication, there
were suggestions for faster-than-light communication, which
contradicted the theory of relativity and was the main point
that Einstein was never able to reconcile himself to.[10] Fortu-
nately, it appears that the world is still in order, at least in this
respect. Assume that Hans wants to send a faster-than-light
message to Franz. Both use a device that can measure the polarization of light waves that have been broadcast in two directions from a source halfway between the two of them. Franz
sets up his measuring device horizontally. A photon in this level
of polarization is either registered or not. Thus, Franz receives
a binary code of zeroes and ones. Hans can set his device up either horizontally or vertically, and the string of signals that
Franz receives will, in fact, depend on how Hans has set up his
device.[11] With this method, Hans can instantaneously influence
the code that Franz receives, but can he send Franz a message?

Recall that the light waves Franz receives are «probability waves,» that the photons arrive according to no particular
rule; Franz receives a random stream. The binary code that he
receives could look like the following:

	Hans horizontal	Hans vertical
Hans	10110100I	10110100I
Franz	10110100I	01001011O

In the first case, Franz always receives a one if Hans sets up a
one, while in the second case the reverse is true. (This is clear,
because the two photons have the same direction of polarization,
which was specified in the setup of the test.) The series of numbers
that Franz receives does in fact depend on what Hans does. But
no matter how Hans positions his device, Franz receives a random
sequence of zeroes and ones. More precisely, Franz receives
various random sequences, depending on how Hans has set up
his device. However, Franz cannot make any use of the influence

exactly because the sequence of zeroes and ones in his message is random. The influence of Hans' decision to set up his machine vertically or horizontally only affects Franz's measurements in the correlation of the two random sequences: 1 for horizontal, -1 for vertical. The mysterious faster-than-light influence could only be discovered by the two by comparing their binary codes, and to do that they would either have to meet or at least call, which is apparently still the best method for exchanging information. It is possible to say that nature communicates faster than light, but bans us from doing it by introducing randomness.[12]

Nevertheless, it is too early to shrug our shoulders and get on with life. There is still a serious proposal for using the effect described here to devise an absolutely spy-proof signaling method[13], as any eavesdropper would influence the message, thus destroying it instantaneously. And it must be admitted that the world's inseparability in macroscopic quantum effects, such as super-conductivity, can be meaningful.

But it is equally premature to fall into mystical holism, to say that everything is connected to everything else, that everything expresses itself in everything else. That would almost mean saying that nature has played a trick on us by inventing quantum mechanical randomness to prevent us from using this wonderful, universal connectedness. It is quite possible that everything is connected but does not express the connection.

And thus it is possible, reader, that you have purchased this magazine only because of an overwhelming yet secret impulse that the universe fulfilled when I wrote these words—and that another possible reader passed it up for precisely the same reason.

NOTES:

1) Anton Zeilinger and his working group at the University of Vienna played a considerable role in these developments. See, for example, B. A. Zeilinger, «Quantum Teleportation,» Scientific American, April 2000, p. 32.

2) W. Heisenberg, Z. Phys. 43, 1927, p. 172

3) Naturally, this has led to some embarrassing mistakes, such as the interlude with cold fusion.

4) E. P. Wigner, «Remarks in the Mind-Body Question,» in I. J. Good, ed., The Scientist speculates, Basic Books, New York 1962

5) A third alternative is known as the theory of leading waves. Originally proposed by Einstein as the «ghost field,» it was supposed to show the wave the path of corpuscular quanta, without having a physical reality itself. This variant, briefly pursued by DeBroglie, never had a chance against the powerful Copenhagen interpretation. In 1950, David Bohm took up a modified form of the idea, but the mathematical successes of the established theory were so considerable that nothing became of leading waves. After Bell's discoveries in 1964 (see later in the main text) interest in this archaic approach increased. Today, some scientists, who should be labeled more epistemologists than physicists, are still prepared to discuss alternatives to the Copenhagen interpretation.

6) In the original German:
> Gar manches rechnet Erwin schon
> mit seiner Wellenfunktion.
> Nur wissen möcht' man gerne wohl,
> was man sich dabei vorstell'n soll.

Quoted in F. Bloch, Physics Today, Dec. 1976, p. 24.

7) J. von Neumann, Mathematische Grundlagen der Quantenmechanik, Springer, Berlin 1932
The passage reads less like a mathematics textbook and much more like excerpts from a philosophical treatise on the problem of the ego. The extent to which physics and philosophy blend into each other can be seen by the existence of titles such as «Existence of Free Will as a Problem of Physics» in serious academic journals. However, publication in physics journals or the presence of well-known names in the bylines is no guarantee that the work is serious. For example, in 1974 on the initiative of Arthur Koestler, a conference on quantum mechanics and parapsychology was held, and world-famous physicists too part along with less widely known parapsychologists. The publication of the conference proceedings contains, among various dubious items, a contribution from H. Puthoff and R. Targ. When Uri Geller was en vogue, these two had «authenticated» his prophetic abilities. From this, one should not conclude that Geller could not prophesy or that QM has nothing to do with unexplained phenomena. However, the conference brought two other factors to light. First, parapsychology is to QM as Uri Geller is to authenticated prediction. Second, the desire for hermetic knowledge is so great, that the critical faculties of even generally critical thinkers can be paralyzed (maybe it should be called paralyzology instead of parapsychology), and that the pseudo-scientific, pseudo-fantastic can

infiltrate a science that is already fantastic enough. It should be noted that there are ten times as many astrologers as astronomers.

8) In contrast to Einstein's thought experiment, this is not concerned with probability waves but with experimental results (film exposures, instrument readings), so that Bohr's objection is not pertinent.

9) More precisely, through 1982 seven experiments were completed, some with electrons, some with photons. The older measurements delivered contradictory results because of insufficient accuracy in measuring. Aspect's experiment was the first one to provide certainty.

10) If faster-than-light communication were possible, signals could be sent to the past, which would cause a considerable commotion. Consider just the opportunities in the stock market. A nice presentation is G. A. Benford, D. L. Book, and W. A. Newcomb, «The Tachyonic Antitelephone,» Physical Review, D 2 (1970): 263-265.

11) This astonishing influence is already recognizable in our simple analogy as the water waves in the pond. We only need to consider the part of the wave that runs from the middle to the opposite shore. As soon as a measurement is taken at a particular point on the shore, a nutshell appears, and the wave also collapses on the opposite side.

12) The experiment is presented here in a simplified form to aid understanding. The results described could also be explained by the assumption that the light source emits not only probability waves but also photons. Only after Hans has chosen between the vertical and horizontal positions are the experimentally verifiable results describable by quantum mechanics. The collapsing probability wave ensures that Hans' decision influences the measurement at the other end of the signal distance. If the condensed history presented here of a problem that has been played out over almost a century shows anything, it is that the expressions that we think of as fixed and certain (such as location, separability, information communication and probability) as loose and uncertain.

13) Quoted from Scientific American, May 1989, p. 20. In the meantime (2004) such signal chains have been made to function over a distance of several kilometers.

Proof of Purchase

---   -

By Marc Calvary

---   -

HOUSE OF BOOKS
565 N. 13TH AVE.
EUGENE, OREGON

TERMINAL I.D.   JH767

MERCHANT #:   3454675890

VISA
XXXXXXXXXXXX0965
EXP.:   08/03
BATCH:000029 INVOICE:0005
DATE:MAR02,03   TIME17:01
           AUTH NO: 006652

SALE

HOW TO WIN FRIENDS AND
                   $13.95

ART OF WAR
                   $10.95

CAR AND DRIVER MAGA
                   $4.95

TOTAL $29.85
CHANGE $0.00

GOLDEN'S MEN CLOTHING
(541) 568-9556
1256 SECOND ST.
PORTLAND   OREGON 97745

QTY/LIST
1   MEN'S HAT STYLE 16   PRICE
                               165.98

1   3PCE SUIT VER
                               665.00

1   LEATHER BRIEFCASE
                               213.00

1   TRAVEL TOIL.CASE
                                24.95

SUB 1068.93 TX 0.00
                        TOT 1068.93
                      CHECK 1068.93
                     CHANGE 0.00

CW0115 TR 222819585 RG 3 03/03/03
       THANKS FOR YOUR BUSINESS
VISIT US ONLINE AT GOLDENSMCAA.COM

MIDTOWN
1256 HIGH ST.

2 APP
$35.95
2 DINNER
$78.95
DRINKS
$38.00
TOTAL:152.90

GRAT: 15.00

TOTAL 167.90
VISA XXXXXXXXXXX1595
EX: 0803

X_____

004012.45
THANK YOU COME AGAIN

AIRWAYS
AIRLINES
AIRWAYSALINE.COM

TICKET
FIRST CLASS
WINDOW
ROUNDTRIP
BUSINESS
TOTAL:
350.00
TX:0.00

TOTAL:
350.00

VISA
000000000000
5956
EXP DATE:
0803

X_____

I AGREE TO PAY ABOVE
TOTAL AMOUNT IN
ACCORDANCE TO CARD ISSUER
AGREEMENT (MERCHANT
AGREEMENT IF CREDIT
VOUCHER)

MERCHANT
COPY

BOOKMARK BARN
1025 N. MANCHESTER
OREGON
(541) 658-5959

QUANITY/DESCRIPTION/LINE PRICE

1   FORTUNE MAGAZINE MAR03 $6.95
1   WALL STREET JOURNAL MAR03 $2.95

SALE
$9.90
CASH
$50.00
CHANGE
$40.10

      DUPLICATE RECEIPT
%DISC. 0.00
CIDNO:25
25.50XSD
03.04.03

MARRIOTT HOTEL
30092355- 1
5852   2025 023

RM 213
SUITE PER NIGHT   159.65

04/04/03 159.65
04/05/03 159.65
04/06/03 159.65
04/07/03 159.65

SUBTOTAL: 638.60

TOTAL:638.60

THANK YOU

glowing in candlelight.

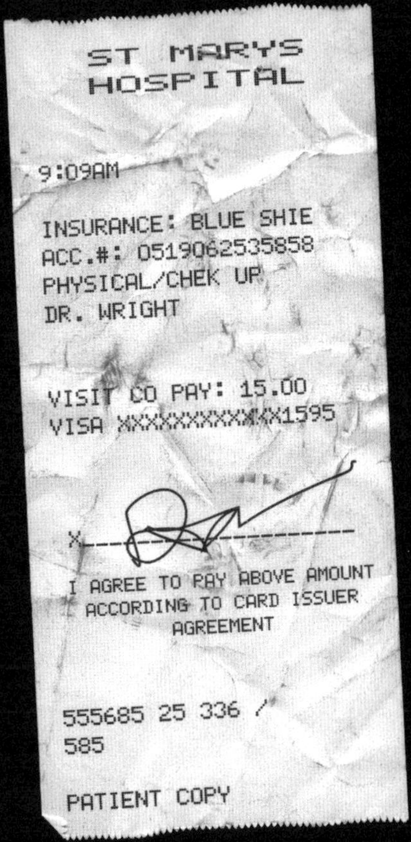
ST MARYS
HOSPITAL
9:09AM
INSURANCE: BLUE SHIE
ACC.#: 0519062535858
PHYSICAL/CHEK UP
DR. WRIGHT
VISIT CO PAY: 15.00
VISA XXXXXXXXXXXX1595
X
I AGREE TO PAY ABOVE AMOUNT
ACCORDING TO CARD ISSUER
AGREEMENT
555685 25 336 /
585
PATIENT COPY

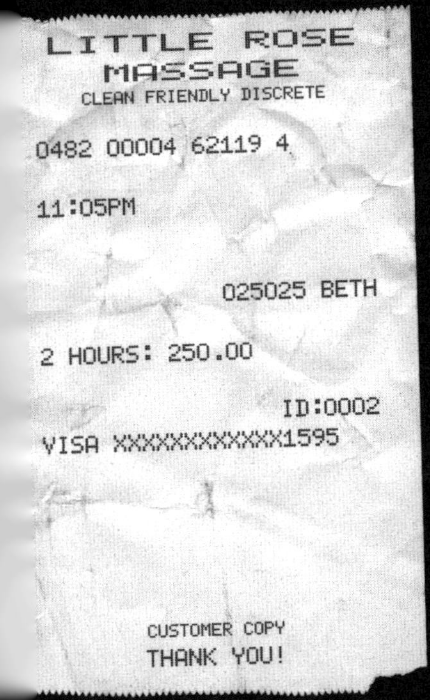
LITTLE ROSE
MASSAGE
CLEAN FRIENDLY DISCRETE
0482 00004 62119 4
11:05PM
025025 BETH
2 HOURS: 250.00
ID:0002
VISA XXXXXXXXXXXX1595
CUSTOMER COPY
THANK YOU!

```
SAV-ALL-DRUG
SAV-ALL-DRUG
SAV-ALL-DRUG #485
85 DIVISION ROAD
541-959-9872

SALE          2585

*************

ACYCLOVIR        59.95
PENCICLOVIR      39.95
VALTREX          57.85
BOOK HERPES      29.95

----------------------

T-ACCOUNT NO:
XXXXXXXXXXXX1595
AUTH:
59858
TYPE:
VISA

X_____
THANK YOU FOR SHOPPING
   AT SAV-ALL-DRUG
```

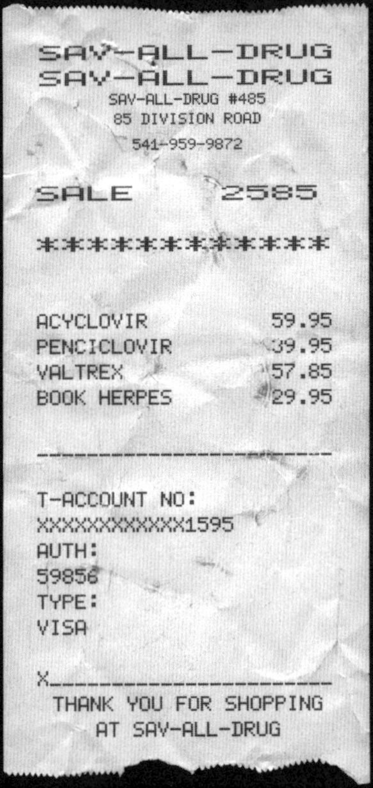

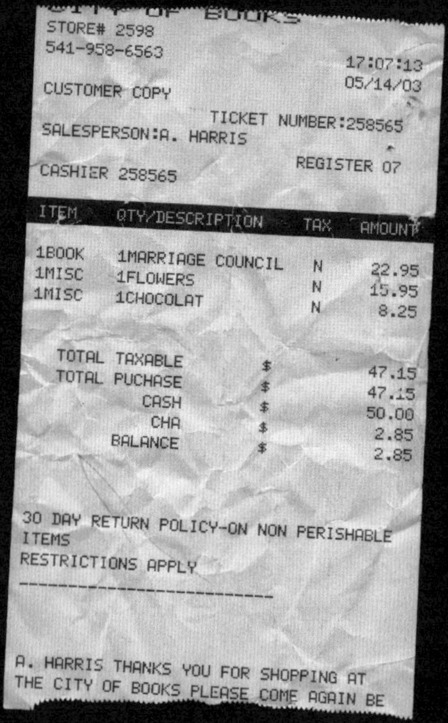

```
CITY OF BOOKS
STORE# 2598
541-958-6563
                        17:07:13
CUSTOMER COPY           05/14/03

           TICKET NUMBER:258565
SALESPERSON:A. HARRIS

CASHIER 258565      REGISTER 07

ITEM   QTY/DESCRIPTION  TAX  AMOUNT

1BOOK  1MARRIAGE COUNCIL  N   22.95
1MISC  1FLOWERS           N   15.95
1MISC  1CHOCOLAT          N    8.25

  TOTAL TAXABLE      $      47.15
  TOTAL PUCHASE      $      47.15
        CASH         $      50.00
        CHA          $       2.85
        BALANCE      $       2.85

30 DAY RETURN POLICY-ON NON PERISHABLE
ITEMS
RESTRICTIONS APPLY
---------------------------

A. HARRIS THANKS YOU FOR SHOPPING AT
THE CITY OF BOOKS PLEASE COME AGAIN BE
```

```
READ ALL OVER BOOKS
   DOWNTOWN BRANCH
   (541) 685-3590


SALE

5852 SURVIVING DEPRESSIO $22.95
----------------------------------
2522 CHICKEN SOUP FOR TH $24.95
----------------------------------
2529 FINDING HOPE IN A H $21.95
----------------------------------
----------------------------------

MASTERCARD
XXXXXXXXXXXX1236
EX:0904
TOTAL          $69.85
CREDIT         $69.85

CUSTOMER COPY
THANK YOU!
```

NOTES

RECEIPT

RECEIVED FROM J. BUTLER LAW OFFICES

ADDRESS 1515 ONYX LANE

6760

FOR CONSULTATION — DIVORCE SERVICES

ACCOUNT		HOW PAID	
AMT. OF ACCOUNT	100 . 00	CASH	100 . 00
AMT. PAID	100 . 00	CHECK	
BALANCE DUE	0 . 00	OTHER	
		TOTAL	100 . 00

BY

which reads:

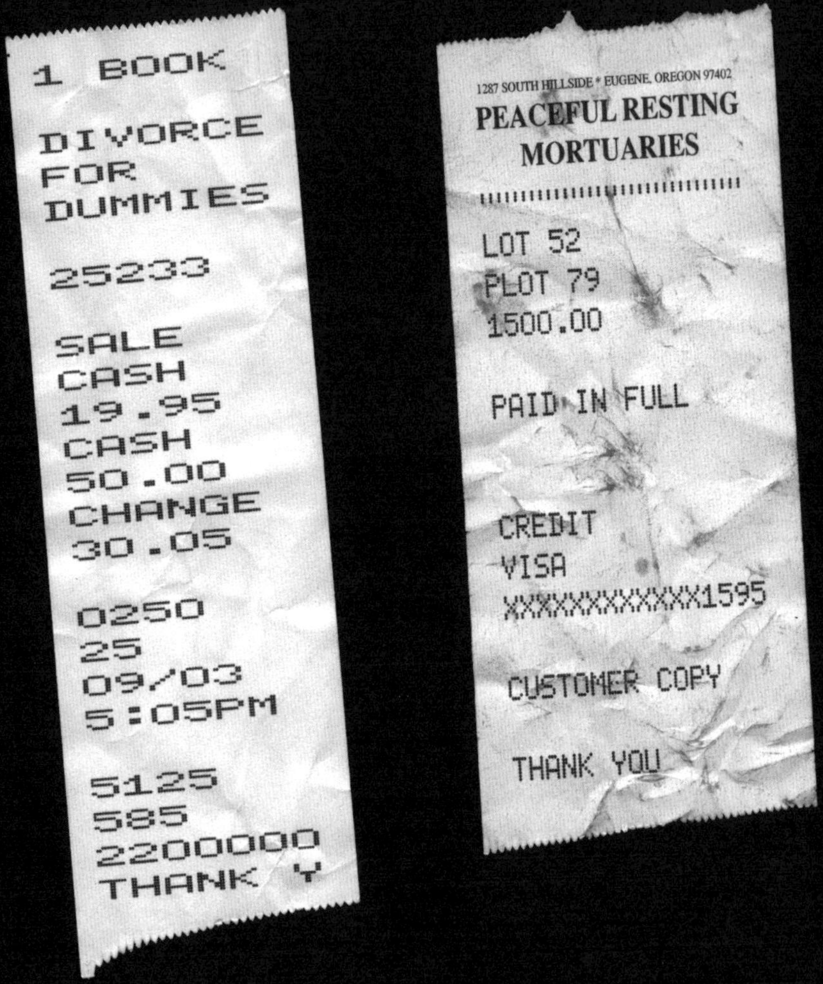
1 BOOK
DIVORCE
FOR
DUMMIES
25233
SALE
CASH
19.95
CASH
50.00
CHANGE
30.05
0250
25
09/03
5:05PM
5125
585
2200000
THANK Y
1287 SOUTH HILLSIDE * EUGENE, OREGON 97402
PEACEFUL RESTING
MORTUARIES
LOT 52
PLOT 79
1500.00
PAID IN FULL
CREDIT
VISA
XXXXXXXXXXXX1595
CUSTOMER COPY
THANK YOU

```
    ....... COPY
    COME AGAIN
 ***************
S-A-L-E-S D-R-A-F-T




  BOTTLE MARKET
 2121 N. JUSKIN




JACK DAN $10.99
***************

CIGARET  $19.95
***************

TOT      20.94
SALE
CASH     50.00
CHGE     19.06


 CUSTOMER COPY
  COME AGAIN
 ***********
S-A-L-E-S D-R-A-F-T
```

```
     HOME AND
    GARDENLAND

    RECEIPT OF
    PURCHASE


9:00AM
REGISTER 16
CASHIER ID:2522


RAT POISON   $8.99
###################

RAT POISON   $8.99
###################
RAT POISON   $8.99
###################

RAT POISON   $8.99
###################
RAT POISON   $8.99
###################

RAT POISON   $8.99
###################
RAT POISON   $8.99
###################

RAT POISON   $8.99
###################

TOTAL       $71.92
CASH        $72.00


  FOR ALL YOUR HOME AND
GARDEN NEEDS PLEASE COME
        AGAIN
```

Portraits of Paradise

By Kessler, Kellas, Mayer

(taken from «The Divine Comedy»

Road notes: or, the ego and the body in northern Georgia

---   ‐

By Jerry Cullum

---   ‐

> *All are prisoners of love and sleep.*
> — the Poimandres of Hermes Three-times Great

> *And here I sit so patiently*
> *Trying to find out what price*
> *You have to pay to get out of*
> *Going through all these things twice*
> > — Bob Dylan, «Stuck Inside of Mobile
> > With the Memphis Blues Again»

> > *This year I hereby resolve to do all the dumb things*
> > *I did last year all over again.*
> > > — «Hagar the Horrible» cartoon

i.   Prisoners of love and sleep

If one lives long enough and is sufficiently willing to look foolish,
every one of one's deepest fantasies will be fulfilled,
although never quite in the exact way
that one imagined them. Fahey's Saint Louis Blues in a room in New Orleans,
just as dreamed and desired years before, lonely in California,
except that this less than drunken Saturday took place during a convention
of the American Academy of Religion. Or Beethoven's Sixth
at the end of a long, reconciliatory week with another unrequited love,
a ridiculous literary device borrowed from an earlier poem, but impossible
to have stage managed because the music was playing
on FM radio. Life, as Oscar Wilde more or less said,
imitates art because, in the end, art is more interesting,
and real life, as a result, gets impossibly jealous.
Actually, Oscar Wilde didn't quite say that. As Bob Dylan so eloquently put it,
I said that.

A lifetime of completely comic questing, more or less defined early on
by fictional characters. I wanted to be Musil's Man Without Qualities,
but unfortunately, my scenarios more typically seem to be written
by Thomas Pynchon as outtakes for Gravity's Rainbow: The Movie.

So here's the critic, as Snoopy would have put it in a Charles Schulz cartoon,
being driven to the big art event by a beautiful woman,
climbing stylishly from the BMW, intent on great thoughts and encounters.
Of course the only real part of all this was the BMW and the beautiful woman.

Here's the critic sitting rumpled in the passenger seat, looking silly as usual.

The one time I saw a visiting British critic whom I will not name,
he was hanging on to the roll bar in some open-topped town version
of a dune buggy, being driven around by some gay artists
determined to impress the guy if it killed both him and them.
It fit his image, and he seemed to be enjoying it,
but I still laughed for hours, in a mixture of pity and envy.

We learn, as Buddha did not say, from other's depressing examples.
Usually, however, all we learn is that this is how you know you've screwed up.

Love and sleep. «I'm not sleep-depraved,» she remarks,
regarding her long night before, spent with others. No, in all truth,
you are not. You are not yet awake, perhaps. «Those who know,
and do not know that they know,
they are asleep: wake them. Those who do not know,
and know that they do not know,
they are in need: teach them. Those who do not know,
and do not know that they do not know, they are fools: avoid them.
But those who know, and know that they know:
through them comes transformation; trust them.»
Slogans of a lost world where wisdom is now supplanted by information,
and information is drowned in a flood of short-sighted passion.
They knew something, once, in regions now clogged with al-Qaida.

Stuck behind a car at the crossroads. «Come on, move!» she says quietly.
Move, indeed, buddy. Some people's reflexes
require a little longer to process sensory information;
as in the joke of bashing the mule with a two by four:
«First thing you have to do is get their attention.»

And we're off. And as usual, I philosophize. At length.

ii. «Hilary stumbles, but the Divine Mind is abundant»
(Ezra Pound, The Cantos)

> *Whether Buddhas arise, O priests, or whether*
> *Buddhas do not arise, it remains a fact and the fixed and*
> *necessary constitution of being that all its components are*
> *delusional.* — Gautama

> *Sometimes I wonder if all the things I've seen*
> *Were ever real, were ever really happening.*
> — Sheryl Crow, «Every day is a winding road»

> *I don't have doubts about your existence.* — God

Thus the billboard that my ambitious unrequited love
interrupts me to point out, saving me from another
probably embarrassing revelation which nobody
particularly wanted. The problem with most of life
is that, as the woman in the New Yorker cartoon put it,
«I do think your problems are significant, Richard.
They're just not very interesting.«

« ‹I,› » as smartass A. Rimbaud put it at age eighteen,
«is somebody else,» the grammatical logic of French dialects
preventing the obvious English answer, «Well, who is you, then?»
Decades after the poet, the pretentious mystic René Guenon
wrote in good Hindu fashion, «René Guenon does not exist.»
And young smartass René Daumal replied, «René Guenon
does not exist? Awww, too bad,» as he had learned from other
remarkable men. And later he wrote a great metaphysical novel,
dying at thirty-six before he could finish. «And you,
what do you seek?» was to be his final chapter heading.
What do we seek? Power, money, sex, the usual.
Or, for us others, a reliable road map out of the world.
Frequently desired in combination with power, money, and sex,
Dante had it right in that regard, about the sequence
in which our failings are discarded in Purgatory.

O, God, sometimes even artistic success is a failure:
The sculpture in Athens of a woman, modeled after wax anatomical figures
from eighteenth century Europe. However, here the exposed heart
is being nibbled by little birdies, creatures which also explode hungrily
from the chest of the twisted male figure, which is also an art history quote.
The anatomies of loss and addiction. Yes, the heart
feeds on itself or twitters hopelessly. The only thing wrong
with this as art, today, is a lifetime of bad science fiction movies.
Damn, the problem even with an obvious message
lies always in finding a satisfactory embodiment,
as, I think, T. S. Eliot and Clement Greenberg and all those dead old farts
probably said sometime back in the previous century.

iii. Athens to Atlanta, or the straight, fast road

If you fall asleep on the road
you'll lose either your hat or your head.
— folk proverb

If you choose, choose to lose
— Nico and the Velvet Underground

«The journey, not the destination,» was a tired cliché of yesteryear,
provoking its pragmatic opposite: «if you don't know where you're going,
any road will take you there.» Baudelaire defined his desired destination:
anywhere better than this burdensome planet.
Athens, Rome, Bethlehem, Berlin, Vienna:
Obviously a lot of the namers of towns in this state
really wanted to be living someplace else.

«Take what you want, but pay for it,»
my father claimed was an old Spanish saying
regarding one's choices in this world.
It is possible to combine sainthood, artistic alienation,
sexual fulfillment and worldly success,
but the price tag on that one is a little steep,
and most of those who scrambled to find the cashier
fell off the glassy upper slopes of Mount Analogue.

You pays your money and you picks your addiction,
drugs, or religion, or wealth, or politics. Lust and greed
govern the planet no matter which you choose.
«O Arjuna, all is clouded by desire,
as a fire by smoke, as a mirror by dust,
with these, it blinds the soul.» Not that Krishna
had a goddam thing to say to most of us slobs
flopping around in the tower of a thousand cloudy mirrors.
No wonder my contemporaries ended up divided
between loonies in this or that gorgeously colored Asian robe
or this or that gorgeously colored running outfit.

«I'll get you there on time, but the curves are bad
and it's going to be a little bumpy.» My bright, sensitive
driver has no suitably neutral noun to describe her,
now that «friend,» «companion,» and any other words you care to name
are euphemisms for sleeping partner. Which she isn't.
I keep quoting her to myself in this misleading fashion
because the problem with self-obsessed interior monologues
is that they leave very little room for the other person
to get an independent word in edgewise.
Someday, like the young woman beloved by Mircea Eliade,
she will write her own version in which I say almost nothing.

«What has Athens to do with Jerusalem?» Tertullian or some other
self-righteous Western saint once said, thus setting forth
the terms of the engagement for the next two millennia
of wars between faith and instrumental reason. The dirty little secret being
that when you get right down to it, you might not want to choose
either of them. Which side are you on, boys. Choose ye this day,
which ye will serve. Labor songs and holy scriptures and graduate students remain in love with binary oppositions: A or not-A, one or zero.

I made my choice, and still don't know where this road is going.
«I can't imagine living in Athens
much beyond puberty,» my whatever she is observes,
and I somehow resist the temptation
for a joke about Plato that would get me clobbered.

> January 13 – 17, 2003
> Feasts of Hilary of Poitiers and Antony of Egypt

---   -

Notes on «Road notes» nine months later

Most poems of the pre-rap era (and some rap lyrics as well) require more
footnotes than there are words in the poem. This one begins with a pun

on the first name of the woman described herein, which I will let remain
a mystery.

I should point out that a running joke in the poem, obscured in any other
language than the original English, is that I have translated foreign terms
unusually: «Hermes Three-times Great» for «Hermes Trismegistus,» for
example, or, later in the poem, «awww, too bad» for the French «hélas» or
«I is somebody else» for Rimbaud's «Je est un autre.»

This poem comes at the end of a long sequence of comic poems of essentially failed pilgrimage: as somebody described a similar quest once,
looking for mystery and ending up with muddle. This is also what happens to the main character in John Crowley's memorable novel Love and
Sleep, from which the Hermetic epigraph has been borrowed; Crowley
describes the whole four-book narrative as a tale governed by the singu-
lar powers of Coincidence, a force which also drives these poems.

John Fahey's guitar solo of «Saint Louis Blues» was popular when I was
living in California, and was part of what propelled me back to the
American South. Therein lies another history of mystery, as with the
other cases cited here ... the point being that most readers of the poem
probably have similar sets of inexplicable, slightly meaningful coincidences in their background. But most people obey the dictum of C. G. Jung's
elderly relative (as translated in Memories, Dreams, Reflections): «Boy,
one doesn't talk about such things.» (The original phrase, in *Erinnerungen
Träume Gedanken* is, I think, an elegant piece of Swiss folk dialect, but I
can no longer locate the passage.)

«I said that»: The Bob Dylan line is found in «Talking World War III
Blues.»

Robert Musil's *Der Mann ohne Eigenschaften* should require no explanation, but Thomas Pynchon's novel may take on a different resonance
when referred to in its standard German translation: not Gravity's
Rainbow but *Die Enden der Parabel*. In neither case does a movie exist, of
course.

A different generation will not catch the resonance of the forlorn fantasy
of Charles Schulz's «Peanuts» cartoon strip, but this reference matters
less than the slip of the tongue in «sleep-depraved» instead of «sleep-
deprived». From this early-morning lapsus linguae, much philosophizing

flows, including the Central Asian dervish recital that is quoted from memory immediately thereafter. Unlike fundamentalist Islam, Central Asian practices were grounded in the same quest for the understanding of mystery found in the Hermetists in the era of Late Antiquity, or in Hilary of Poitiers, the medieval philosopher to whom the line from Ezra Pound refers (quoted in the title of part ii).

René Daumal's «great metaphysical novel» of symbolic mountain climbing is Le Mont Analogue. The «Athens» in which the life-size wax sculpture by the Philadelphia artist Kris Balogh was on exhibit is the home of the University of Georgia, though its more famous namesake, the home of the 2004 Olympics, comes into play in the poem very quickly.

Mircea Eliade's roman a clef about his youthful romance in India is La Nuit Bengali; his abandoned lover Maitreyi Devi wrote her own story decades later in the novel It Does Not Die. «Which Side Are You On» is a famed labor organizing song by Joe Hill, transmuted years later by Arlo Guthrie into a metaphysical parable. I trust the implicit closing joke about platonic love needs no further explanation, but I have typically been wrong about such things.

The Zugun Case

---   -

By men on the moon

---   -

Synopsis

One day in the winter of 1925 in a remote area of Romania the twelve-year-old Eleonore Zugun walked through a forest. She was accompanied by her elder male cousin and on her way to visit her blind great-grandmother who was more than one hundred years old and lived in the neighboring village. In the forest the girl found a coin and picked it up although her cousin had warned her according to an old Romanian superstition it was devil's money. Still she kept the coin and, arriving in the village, spent it on candies. She then ate them without offering any to her female cousin who lived with the great-grandmother. Thereupon the old woman said that Eleonore had «swallowed» the devil. He now was within her body.

These words acted like a curse: On the very next day stones were thrown against and into the house from the outside by invisible powers, and objects in Eleonore's vicinity mysteriously moved through the air. The girl was sent back to her home village—with the only result that the phenomena continued there after a break of three days. At a later stage, the strange forces even left scratches in her face and spit at her. She was subsequently called «the devil's girl» in Talpa.

Soon the news of the case was spread throughout the whole country. They were also heard within the circles interested in the study of such phenomena. Enter Countess Wassilko whose family originated from Romania. When the then thirty-year old Countess, who had a long-standing interest in psychical phenomena, learned about a poltergeist case taking place on «her own» territory she visited Talpa. There she soon decided to invite the girl to Vienna in order to study her phenomena thoroughly.

The very next day after Eleonore had arrived there the maid allegedly saw a silver spoon falling down from the table by itself. From then on the Countess wrote down each and every phenomenon around Eleonore. She identified two distinct phases when after six months the locomotion of small objects gradually shifted to dermal phenomena such as scratches and bites on the girl's skin or spitting at her.

The Countess then took Eleonore on a five-month «tour» through London, Berlin, Nuremberg and Munich to visit leading parapsychologists. During that time log files were kept by different witnesses and at the end of the journey a movie was shot which shows Eleonore's dermographic phenomena.

When Eleonore returned to Vienna she experienced her menarche. After that the phenomena quickly decreased and soon disappeared completely. Eleonore stayed with the Countess for one more year and was instructed in hairdressing in order to be able to support herself when she got back home to Romania. Never again did she experience mysterious phenomena, but from then on led an uneventful life.

Das abergläubische
Bauernkind führt die
Verletzungen auf den
Teufel (rumänisch
„Dracu") zurück

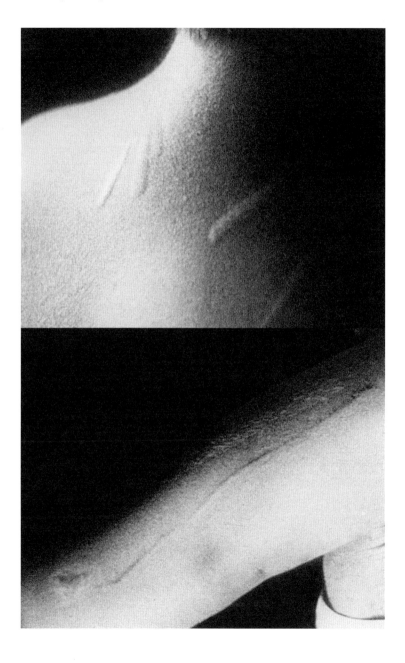

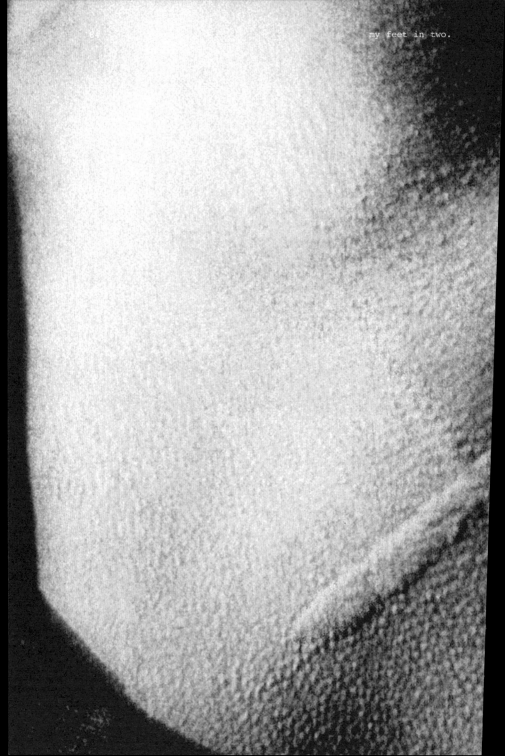
my feet in two.

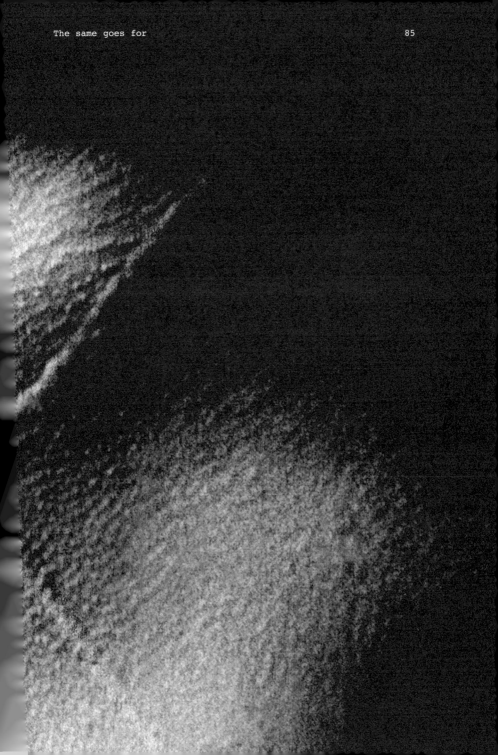

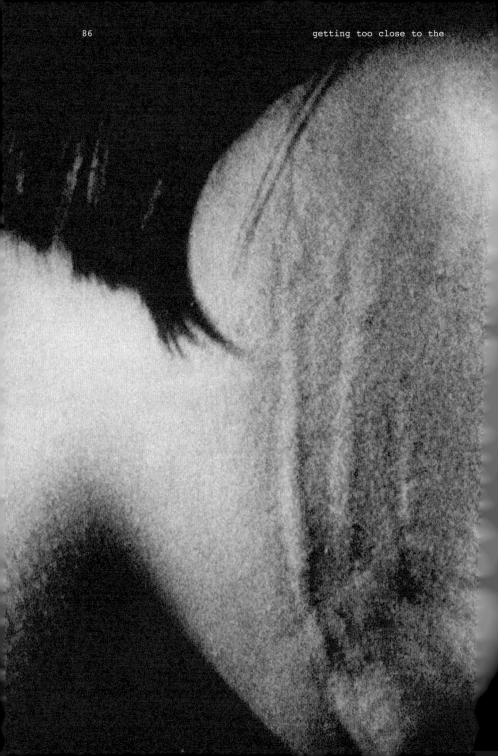

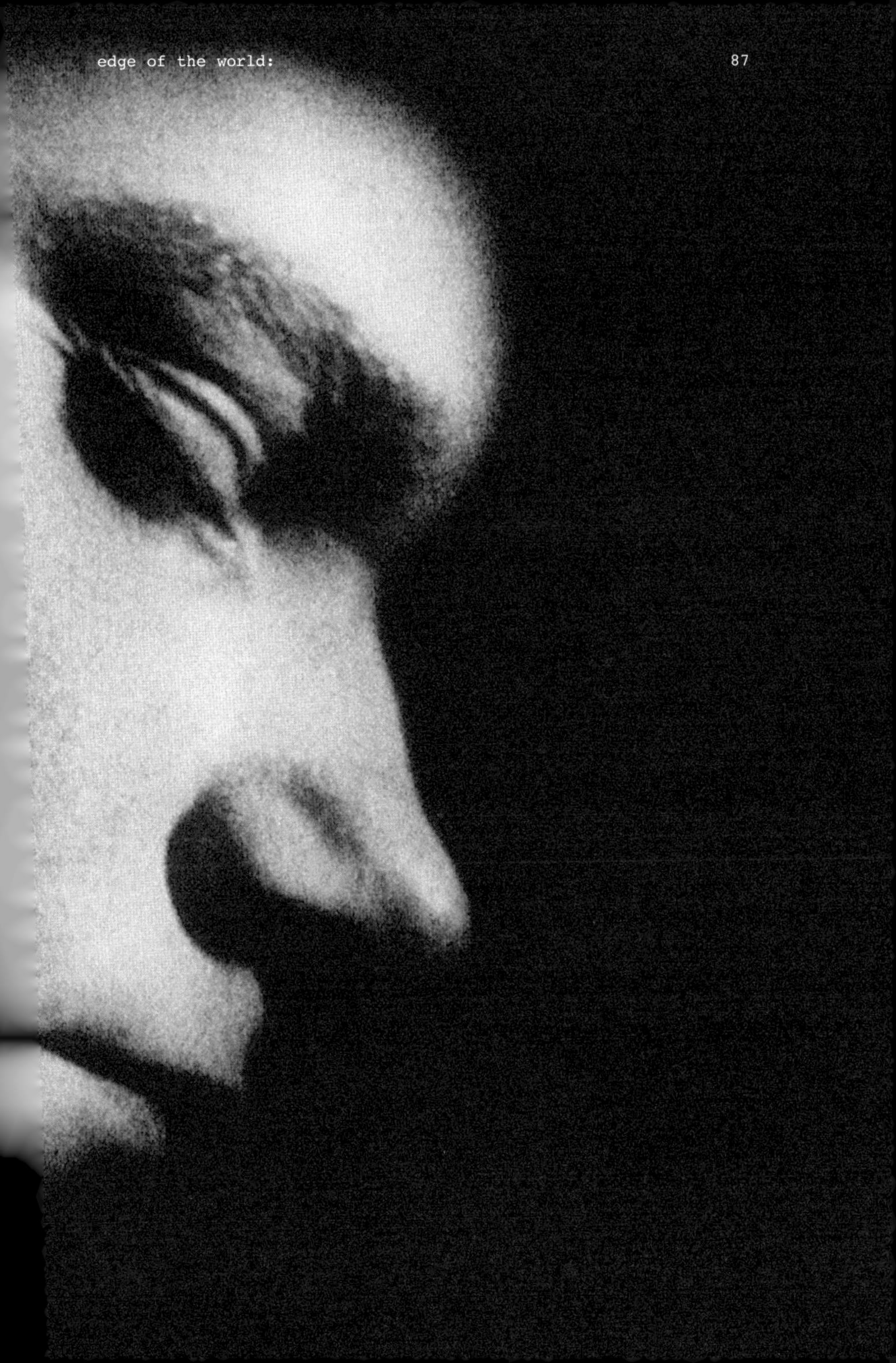

Dieser Film ist der vor-
läufige Abschluß einer
langen Untersuchungs-
reihe wissenschaftlicher
Autoritäten in Wien,
London und Berlin.
Vergleiche den Sammel-
bericht in No. 8 der Ärzt-
lichen Rundschau 1927

Scientific interpretation by Prof. Peter Mulacz

The «poltergeist» phenomena occurring in Eleonore Zugun's presence started out with inexplicable movements of various objects. Stones were thrown from a nearby river into the house by an unknown force, shattering the windows. After observers had marked the stones and brought them back to the river, they mysteriously reappeared inside the house. No one could follow how they traveled the eighty-meter distance.

By the superstitious peasant population these phenomena were attributed to the devil—in Romanian «Dracu». The cousin's idea of the «devil's money» and particularly the great-grandmother's remark that Eleonore had «swallowed» the devil were of vital importance for the case. Thus the «Dracu» became a personification in Eleonore's subconscious—a person within a person. This was accompanied by a severe guilt complex as it was later revealed by psychoanalysis.

In Vienna the phenomena were much less violent than in Romania. No more stones were thrown, yet small objects continued to disappear and to reappear elsewhere or to move around as if they were animated. Interestingly enough the direction of these motions was always towards the girl, which may be seen as auto-aggressive acts connected to her guilt complex.

During the second phase of Eleonore's mediumship dermographic phenomena came to the fore. By coincidence, she suffered from a hypersensitivity of her skin which is a rather frequently occurring abnormity. Scratches and bite marks that appeared on her face, neck, arms, and décolleté developed weals within minutes. These wounds originated from the «outside» — as opposed to stigmata in the religious sense which emerge from the depth of the tissue. In either case the marks result from mental images deeply rooted in the unconscious of the respective person, but in the Zugun case they took a detour through the «outside world» — which is the very essence of psychokinesis.

Although the Countess Wassilko's five-month «tour» with Eleonore reminds a bit of a traveling circus it seemed important to have a strong medium perform in front of several highly qualified researchers independent from one another. Thus this case has gained considerable public evidence that could be matched only more than thirty years later by the Rosenheim case. Finally the EMELKA film company in Munich recorded a documentary early in 1927. It was one of the first instances of documentary cinematography applied to a topic within the field of parapsychology. As an after-effect of the Zugun case the team involved in the investigation formed the «Austrian Society for Psychical Research» (now: «Austrian Society for Parapsychology and Border Areas of Science»).

Watch the original documentary of «The Zugun Case» at: www.rosebudmagazine.com

Nazca Drawings

By Janusz Daga

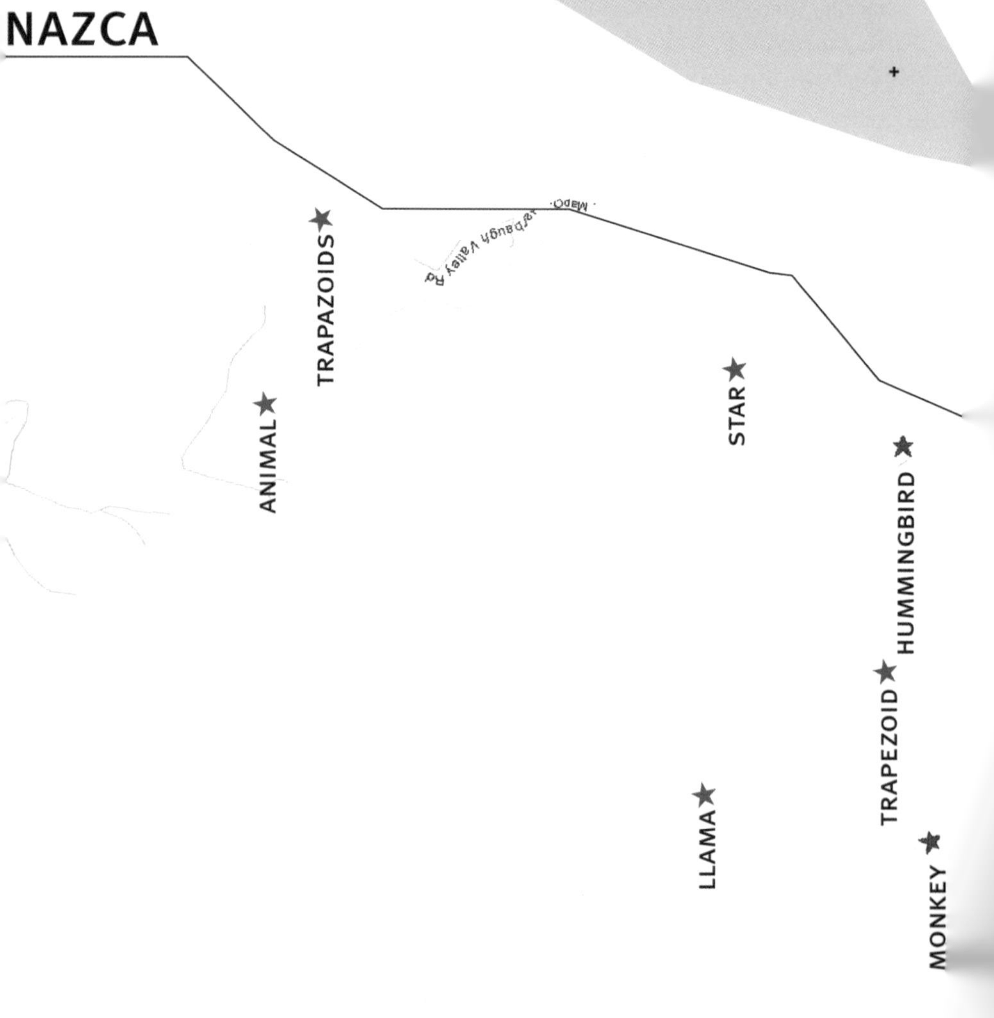

NAZCA

Map: Harbaugh Valley Rd.

TRAPAZOIDS ★

ANIMAL ★

STAR ★

HUMMINGBIRD ★

TRAPEZOID ★

LLAMA ★

MONKEY ★

\+

\-

The Nazca Lines are an engima.

No one knows who had built them or indeed why.
Do these huge geoglyphs, etched into the surface of the
desert, originate from a long extinct civilization?
Do they indidicate the existence of an alien universe?
In my mind the geometric forms become alive,
starting to transform into another universe.

My universe.

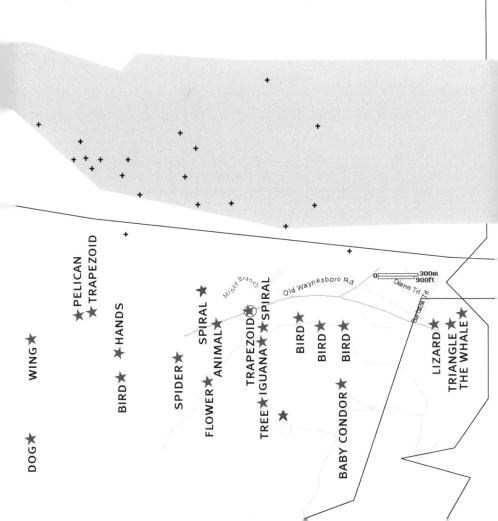

FIJI

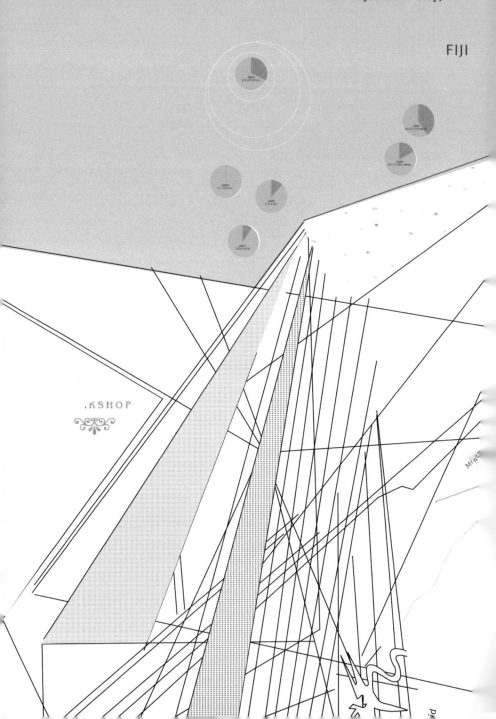

.KSHOP

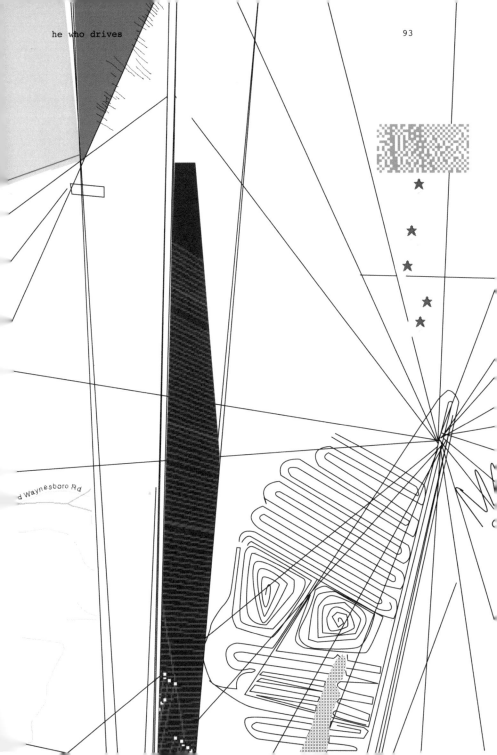

trapzoid

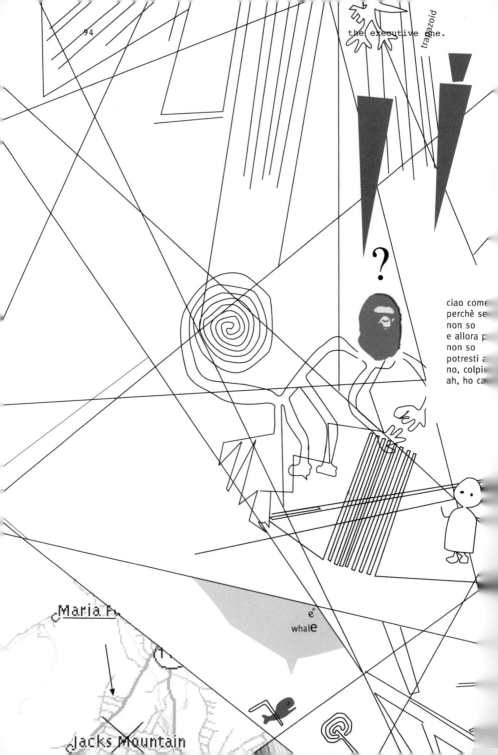

?

ciao come
perchè se
non so
e allora p
non so
potresti a
no, colpi
ah, ho ca

Maria F

e°
whal e

Jacks Mountain

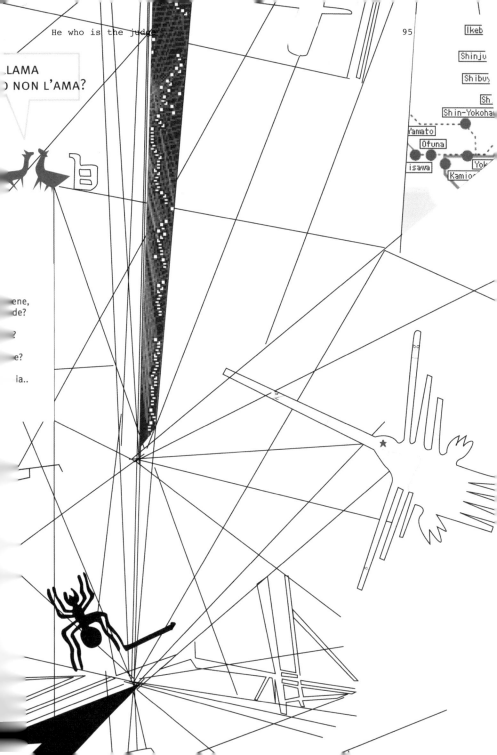

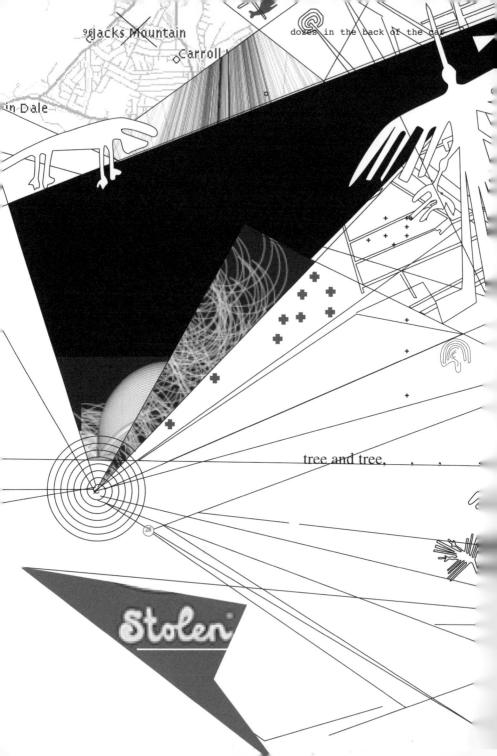

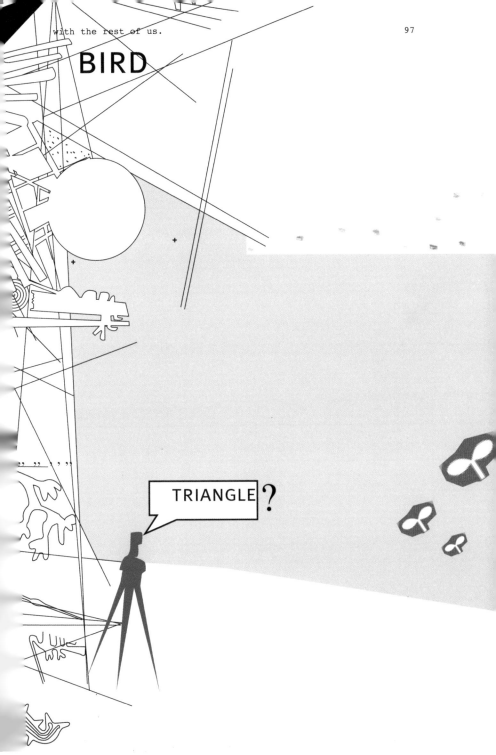

A Long Time Ago
There Was...

---   –

By Interkool — Sabine Feichtner and Christoph Steinegger

---   –

... Is it any wonder

Do onto neighbors

Found Notes

---   -

Collected by Anna Gerber, Marc Kulicke and Lisa Marshall

---   -

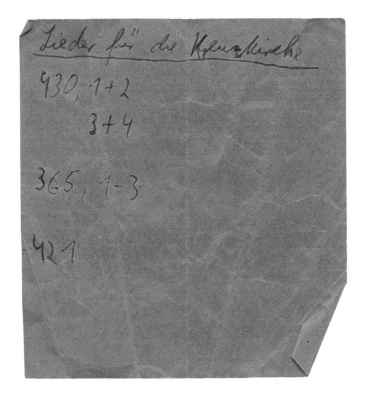

1.   «No truth but in things.» —William Carlos Williams

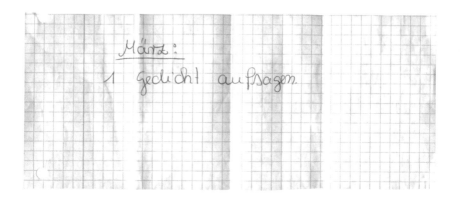

2.   We find a mundane, (seemingly) meaningless object and a transformation occurs. We claim it as our own. And through this claiming, this immediate sense of ownership, we inject the object with meaning. And we start to imagine stories and previous lives... We inject objects with value. We assign them a sort of importance. A relevance. Perhaps one that even reflects our own lives. And suddenly the object becomes something other.

3.   A few months ago, I found a bit of beautiful cream and red floral 1940's wallpaper sticking out from behind my radiator. I've kept it, archived it, and every time I look at it, I ponder its meaning—I ask myself what was here before. What story does a space contain before it becomes yours? Before you become part of its memory?

4.   There's a book made up of found notes called «Concerning the Poetry of Lost Things.» Notes—fragments of shopping lists, daily reminders, bits of suicide notes—when brought together start to form a narrative. A story emerges of other peoples' moments. Peoples' remnants come together to tell a story of our (their) everyday. A collection of the mundane comes together and becomes something else.

5.   «It is to the unknown that one yields most impulsively; it is toward the unknown that one feels the most total, the most instinctive obligation.» —Jean Baudrillard

6.   I am walking down a dark street late at night and see a single shoe lying there. Lying there as though a person would. As if I can see the person lying there, still connected to, still somehow belonging to the shoe. But the person has continued somewhere else. And left the shoe behind as a sort of relic. A piece of evidence. A reminder. A(nother) story.

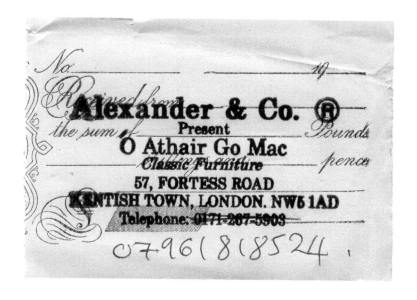

7.   I think about following people. Tracing their steps.
Looking for their stories. Who they are, where they're going.
Sophie Calle followed a man from Paris to Venice. And docu-
mented it with photographs. And somehow these followings,
these strangers' lives remind me of finding things. How you
look for clues. For evidence. And how it's always about stories.
About inventing stories that already exist in one form, that we
simply transform into another.

8.   I start to think about what we choose to find. Why does a note, someone's handwriting, the trace of someone's life, a glimpse of someone else's moment mean anything to us? We judge our findings. We select. We prioritize. We qualify them as «beautiful,» or not. We find only what we deem worth finding.

9.   «Photographs are of course artefacts. But their appeal is that they also seem, in a world littered with photographic relics, to have the status of found objects—unpremeditated slices of the world.» — Susan Sontag

10.   Scraps, found objects, memories, things, bits... We grow
attached to these «things,» these seemingly meaningless objects, often feeling a compulsion to hang onto them, to keep
them. In archiving this flotsam, this jetsam, we are keeping
these «things» alive, active. And in turn, if left to gestate, if re-
visited at random, if left to evolve in the dark, they inspire, provoke, even materialize into (other) ideas, into new things, new
versions of their earlier incarnations.

This collection of objects and thoughts look at the
everyday mysteries of found objects: notes, scraps
of paper, photos found lying on the streets of London,
Berlin and Vancouver.

Oddly enough, the process that brought all of this
work together had its own mystery, dictated by a
strange kind of chance.

Shortly after submitting my contribution about found
objects, I learned that +rosebud had received a
similar concept just days before from Germany. An
avid collector of found objects had also proposed to
create a story based on his findings. About two weeks
later, having heard about a piece +rosebud was doing
on «found objects,» Lisa Marshall sent in the «Repent
Sinner» cardboard sign she had found in Vancouver.
What followed was a chance collection in the most real
sense: one that brings together strangers from around
the world and the mysterious objects they found.

                                              Anna Gerber

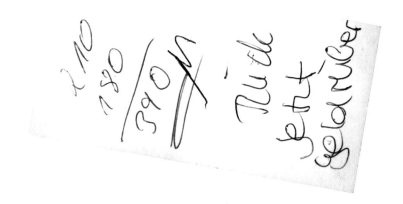

Birds

---   -

(I Don't Need a Rainbow to Show Me the Way)

---   -

By Alexander Egger

The Society of Electronic Voice Phenomena Researchers

---   –

A Documentation by Ernst Schmiederer
with Photos by Thomas Smetana

---   –

The Society's meeting room in Vienna's Eisvogelgasse. Tuesday
evening. A table, coffee cups, an ashtray. Two women are reading transcripts of a tape recording. In parallel, their Walkman
keeps repeating the same, very brief portion of the recording.
Snippets of voices can be heard, foreign languages, the noises of
a radio changing frequencies. Otherwise nothing, or so a visitor
might think. The two women hear more.

«Rudi. Did you hear it? That was Rudi.» The two women
associate the voice, heard briefly, with one of their husbands,
with Rudi. Rudi's widow says, «Are you sure? In January it'll be
three years since he died. But did you hear it? Rudi. A chill went
up my spine when I heard that, I got goose bumps. Rudi.»

Maria Manov, Chairwoman

We meet here every Tuesday at six in the evening. Relaxed, with coffee. But at seven, precisely, we start. We're written in as the group that starts at seven. The Vienna group is seven o'clock on Tuesday. They know that on the other side. Sometimes they tell us we're late.

Let's get the basics down. My maiden name is Stacher, and my family were all doctors or teachers. We have two professors of medicine in the family. My husband was an opera singer, a soloist. At the end he had his own ensemble, and they only sang music from the Orthodox church. It was beautiful. Orthodox, from the East. My husband came from Bulgaria.

He died in 1995. Quite suddenly. Three weeks and he was gone. And that makes a person wonder, makes you think that something has to still be there. Plus in the 70s I met a Bulgarian medium. A blind woman. An excellent medium.

Anyway, in November 1995 I was at a congress for transcommunication, and they were talking about voices on tape, but also about mediums, computer messages and pictures on videotapes. Everything. There were really great people there, people like Professor Senkowski. I had studied his books. Over time I made contacts among the German researchers. We had some very nice meetings. We traveled to Egypt, where we practiced in the Great Pyramid. Very good times.

One day I sat down and called on certain spirits myself. And look, I got them on tape.

Father Leo Schmidt, for example. He says, «Schmidt, hear the dead.» Those was his dictum, Schmidt, hear the dead. I also got an answer from Manfred Boden, Charlie they called him, and he had worked quite a bit in this field. Peter Haerting, the husband of a very dear friend. Friedrich Juergenson spoke up, the pioneer of taped voice research. Dr. Konstantin Raudive. I have them all on tape. I've got piles of tapes and recordings, from Einstein to Khrushchev.

My husband spoke up, too. He told me that the first few times, someone else had answered for him. Obviously, he couldn't yet do it at that time. Technically, it's very difficult. The ones on the other side have to speak into a «voice box» so that it reaches us. And not everyone can do it. That's why they are often represented by someone else.

The first thing that my husband said to me was the following: «Make me crazy happy the fact with you.» He meant the fact that we were in contact. From that he knew that I knew about him and he knew about me. That was a comfort. Then another time I heard, «don't cry, I live.» Then «Khere's Manov,» with the Slavic accent coming through in «khere» so that you would recognize it was him. «I see you all,» with the accent too. That gave a chill to all of his Bulgarian friends I played the tape for.

Eventually it goes further. You want to know who the guardian spirit is, the spirit guide. You hear things like, «Maria, you should pray, Maria, you don't pray at all, in the morning, Maria, go and pray. Maria, God loves you truly.» Or, «Adonis loves you truly, good God, he loves you from the bottom of his heart.» It's ecumenical. «The Koran is useful, too.» That's how someone named Ali spoke up. I didn't know who this Ali was, but then I learned that he was the Prophet's son-in-law. «The Koran is useful, too.»

I'm Catholic myself. I don't really need any religion just for itself. This work definitely raises the question of who or what is God. God is everything that is. Everything. And the ones on the other side, those are ours that were here on earth and died. We get advice from the other side. And neither they nor we want us to make a big fuss about it.

Maria Manov:
«I knew a very nice man in an electronics business. He understood my efforts, and he always let me try out different microphones.»

Maximilian Kvacsik, Sound Engineer

Look at this, we've got two short wave radios here. The point is to make sure you have some foreign tape. Yugoslav, Russian, it definitely ought to be something durable like that. I have to change the stations while I'm doing it, so that I only get words, I don't want to have any music on it.

Here we've got a normal recording device, a basic cassette deck. Plus a machine for playing it back. In our case, it's a modified car radio. You might ask, why an old car radio? Well, it has more robust parts, and it's been specially modified for our purposes.

Finally, we need a timed switch for interrupting the tape mix, so that we get five seconds from each station. Down there is the thing we call the Tremolant, which you can use to switch from one Hertz up to 25 Hertz. You'll know that from music, it's the Lesly Effect, the guitarist's tremolo.

That's all.

We broadcast the taped material, the foreign radio station that is, out into space. And the people ask their questions. We record the whole thing. And after they're all finished with their questions, we play it back. And there is supposed to be something on it.

Maximilian Kvacsik:
«The people ask their questions. We record the whole thing.
And after they're all finished with their questions, we play it back.
And there is supposed to be something on it.»

Anton Rosenberger, Survivor

I really owe everything to the Society. Especially our Mrs. Manov. She tells me everything that can be heard on the tapes, because I don't hear so well anymore.

I came to it just by chance. One day my brother called me up. «Tony,» he said, «Turn your TV on, there's a program on, there's someone saying there's life after death.» Well, that was a film about this, about our Society.

When I came here the first time, it was explained to me that this Society was founded to help people who had lost a special person. I had a very, very happy marriage. Was married 47 years. Then a sudden illness. My wife had cancer, dear God, a very bad one. She died of it. And I was finished, wanted to take my own life.

By pure coincidence… although there's no such thing as coincidence… anyway, I was brought here. Unfortunately, the first time I tried to make contact with my wife, I didn't get an answer. A very nice lady came to me and said, «Mr. Rosenberger, please don't cry. Someone will tell your wife that you called, and she will be here the next time.» I was excited about the following Tuesday, and she was there the next time.

I asked my questions. «Please give me a message. I hug you and kiss you, love, Tony.»

And she answered. «Anton, my love, I love you.»

I thought to myself, well, anyone could say that. But then she said, «Tony, Mary, news.» That meant, «Tony, tell Mary,» that was her sister, «that I'm alive.» Well, I was completely moved. Nobody here knew about Mary.

Anton Rosenberger:
«You can't talk to people about it. People are ignorant, and when someone talks about such things, they give a dumb answer. He's nuts, they say. When someone is dead, he's dead, they say. So foolish. People don't know that everyone has a soul and a second body, the so-called astral body, which rises up when the earthly life ends.»

Then there were other times when I asked, please, can you help me, I'm really suffering from heartburn. And she named a particular medicine. I went to the pharmacy, and the person there said that was a medication against heartburn. Isn't that amazing? Another time she said to me, Tony, you don't hear so well, you need help with your hearing. The next day, the doctor gave me a prescription for a hearing aid.

These days, I really feel healthy and good. I've become a person again, I enjoy life again. I couldn't have gone on like I was before, when you wake up in the morning and the bed next to you is empty. It's terrible, I don't want to live through that kind of thing again. But now I know, my wife is waiting for me, she says that to me quite often, and that's why I believe.

Eduard and Edith Koeckeis, Pioneer and his Shadow

I have been doing it since 1978, long before there was a Society here. There was a small group with engineer Seidl, every Monday in a coffeehouse downtown. There were technicians there who had cobbled the machines together. That's where I met Mr. Luksch, who was Chairman for a long time. Then the circle kept getting bigger. We started with sessions in extra rooms, there were often 40 people there. Separately, we had a smaller group of people trying different approaches with various methods and machines. The circle kept getting bigger. Mr. Seidl, the engineer, did not want to found a Society. Mr. Luksch wanted one, though, so that we would have a place to store the machines.

Eduard and Edith Koeckeis:
«That is my wife,» he says. «The shadow,» she says. The shadow?
«Yes, because I am with him everywhere,» says Edith. «I come along with my husband. I go with him. Every Tuesday.»

Today we are not doing any more research. In a smaller group, we asked questions, worked out an approach. When Mr. Luksch read in the paper that there had been a murder, he tried to find the murderer by asking questions. Then he left the list with a lawyer. Out of ten cases of murder, in seven of them he had the name of the murderer on the tape. But the police were not very interested. Then he gave up, because he just wanted to show that this phenomenon of recorded voices exists.

Since then, the circle has grown smaller. Interest is fading. There used to be young people involved, now there aren't any really. It used to be more interesting to me, the technical aspects.

I started with a normal reel-to-reel tape machine, with a normal microphone and no amplifier. I got good results with that setup. Senta Morina, the Dr. Raudive's secretary announced herself as a go-between. The lady had been paralyzed, in a wheelchair, then she died, and I got a connection with her. That lasted half a year.

Today, we have amplifiers, so the voices can be picked out a bit more clearly. The machines are better, the reception. But the voices don't get better. I don't believe that the technology plays a role at all. It's energies that play a role, not technology.

I have had certain experiences, in the course of time, like when my wife died; we (Mr. Koeckeis gestures to Edith, his second wife) got married not too long ago, three years.

I made attempts myself, when my wife died. I had hoped that I would receive some messages. Unfortunately, that did not come to pass. I got her name, made contact, it couldn't have been anyone but her because nobody else knows the personal references.

But otherwise, I didn't receive anything more substantive from my wife, nothing that would have been interesting. Just this, «Have no fear, I am behind you.» Most recently I heard, «You cannot reach her, she has attained another level, she has passed over to another dimension.» There are various levels on the other side.

(Mr. Rosenberger speaks up): There is the waiting room of heaven, supposedly there are seven dimensions, and my wife was apparently in the third. That's where most of them are, at least the ones who have lived decently. They keep improving themselves, they are learning up there. We know that from the recorded voice researchers.

(Mr. Koeckeis continues): I called Mr. Luksch and asked why he isn't responding. He was always saying that when he passed over to the other side, he would be in touch. But nothing has come through yet. He has been dead since 1991 or '92. And we haven't heard anything substantial from him yet.

Darko and Xenia Horwat, Parents

Mr. Horwat: It's very important to have positive energy. Without positive energy, nothing works. The technology is meaningless, in and of itself. It's good if you have a tape machine that you can repeat with, that's important for listening afterward. Normally, you don't understand the first time you listen, but then if you repeat it two or three times afterward, then you understand the voice. What interests me is not the main voices but the background noises. MP3 is too compressed, the background voices get lost. I had bad experiences with MP3, it's compressed too far, it's not suitable. I have a completely normal Philips recorder that cost 100 Euro. That was worth it. Philips D 64.

There are several methods. For beginners, it's good to take a carrier that broadcasts in a foreign language. German isn't suitable because it's a distraction. A language you don't know at all is suited best. In the breaks of these languages — you have to know the rhythm of a language to be able to gauge the breaks better — in the breaks you hear voices. You're always running into the danger that you recognize something in the foreign language that's not the message.

We have been involved for two and a half years, since the death of our son. He was 19 years old, and he died. As an inheritance, he left us one word: hyperspace. We bought a book and read about hyperspace. Then we got in contact with Professor Mecklenburg in Germany, and he put us in touch with Mr. Senkowski. And he said to me, there is a Society. The first time, our second son came too. Our son on the other side spoke to him with internet chat nicknames — no one else knew them.

Hyperspace. I will die soon and be in hyperspace. He knew that he would die. He died from a brain hemorrhage.

Mrs. Horwat: If I might interrupt just for a moment. My son knew that he would die. A year before he died, he asked, «Mami, what is the meaning of life?» I couldn't answer. He said, «Listen to me carefully. In a year, I will die, but don't be sad, I will be with you more then than I am now. I will be in hyperspace.» That was the decisive word. At the time, I didn't know what it meant. A year later, he really died. He also said, «Mami, we are not mistaken, in a year I will be gone.» It's a fact: We spoke the day before Christmas, and the day before Christmas he died.

The first sentence that he sent was, «I'm alive.» He died the day before Christmas 1999. In March 2000, I heard him for the first time, «I'm alive.»

Darko and Xenia Horwat:
«*Nobody hears everything, and sometimes it comes too fast. That's when your own tape helps, so that you can hear the things that you would miss otherwise,*» *he says.*
«*When I got up this morning, I had completely red eyes. Mary and Josef I said, I can't see a thing! But now it's a little better,*» *she says.*

Hauff

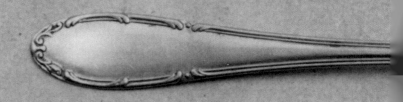

look!

www.hauff.sk

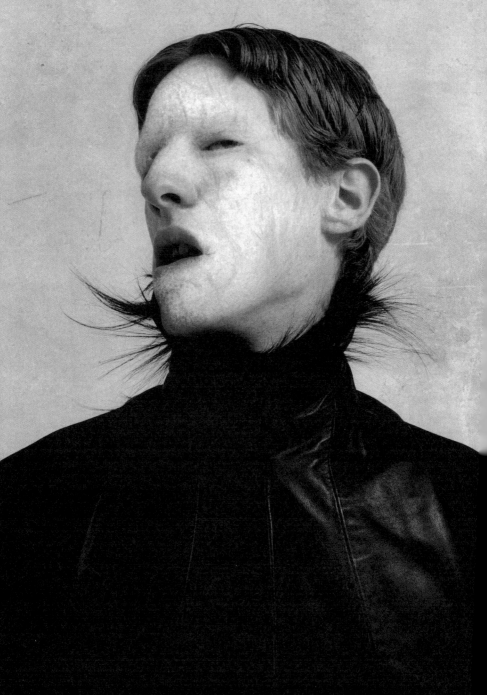

There is a secret

there is a place

follow the sisters

and enter the Maze

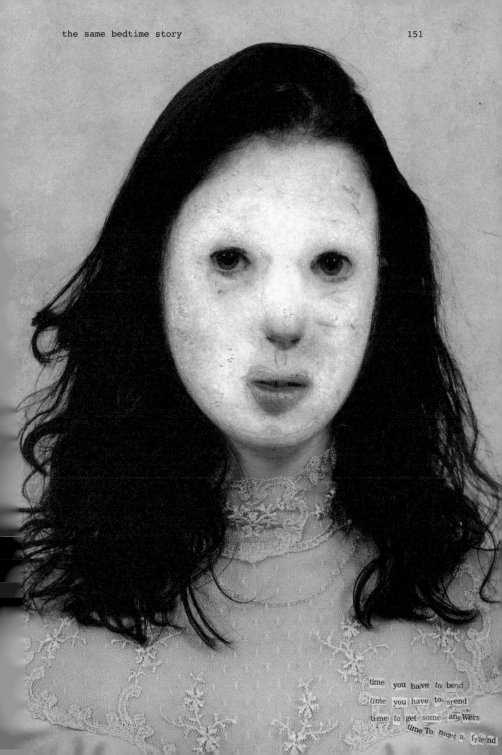

time you have to bend
time you have to spend
time to get some answers
time To meet a friend

where
152
where flying things in water stand
where moving things the others reach
where madness takes the lonely hard
some comfort lurks beyond the beach

over and over again.

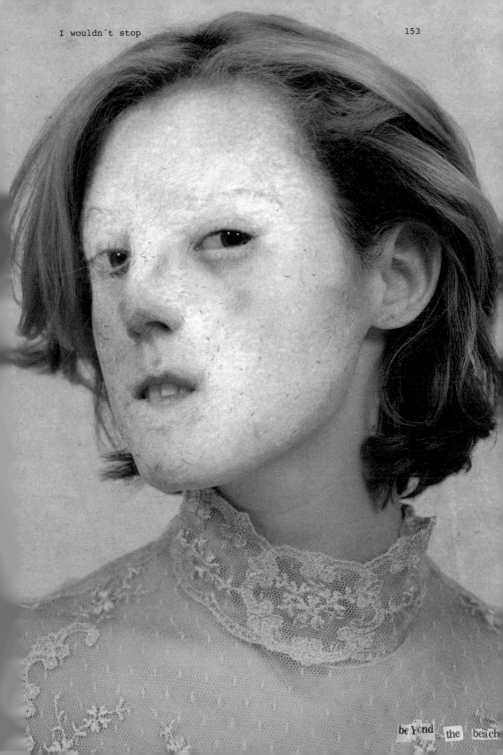

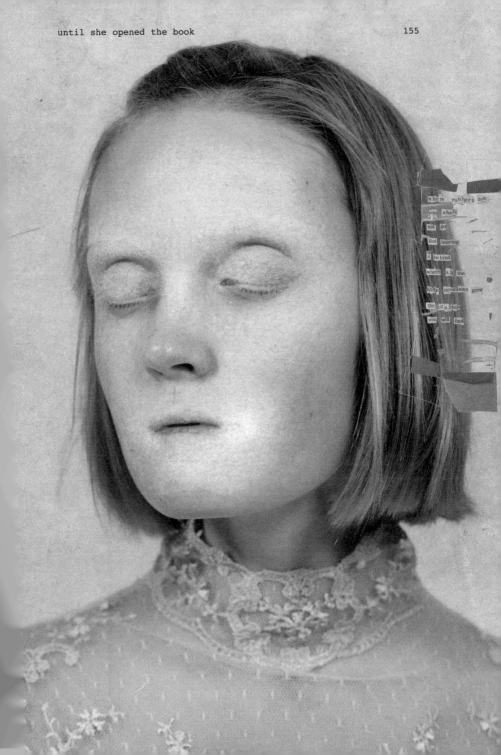

where robbers are
you shall
not go
But leaving
it behind
where a li the
little mountains grow
the sign from
you will find

and started to read

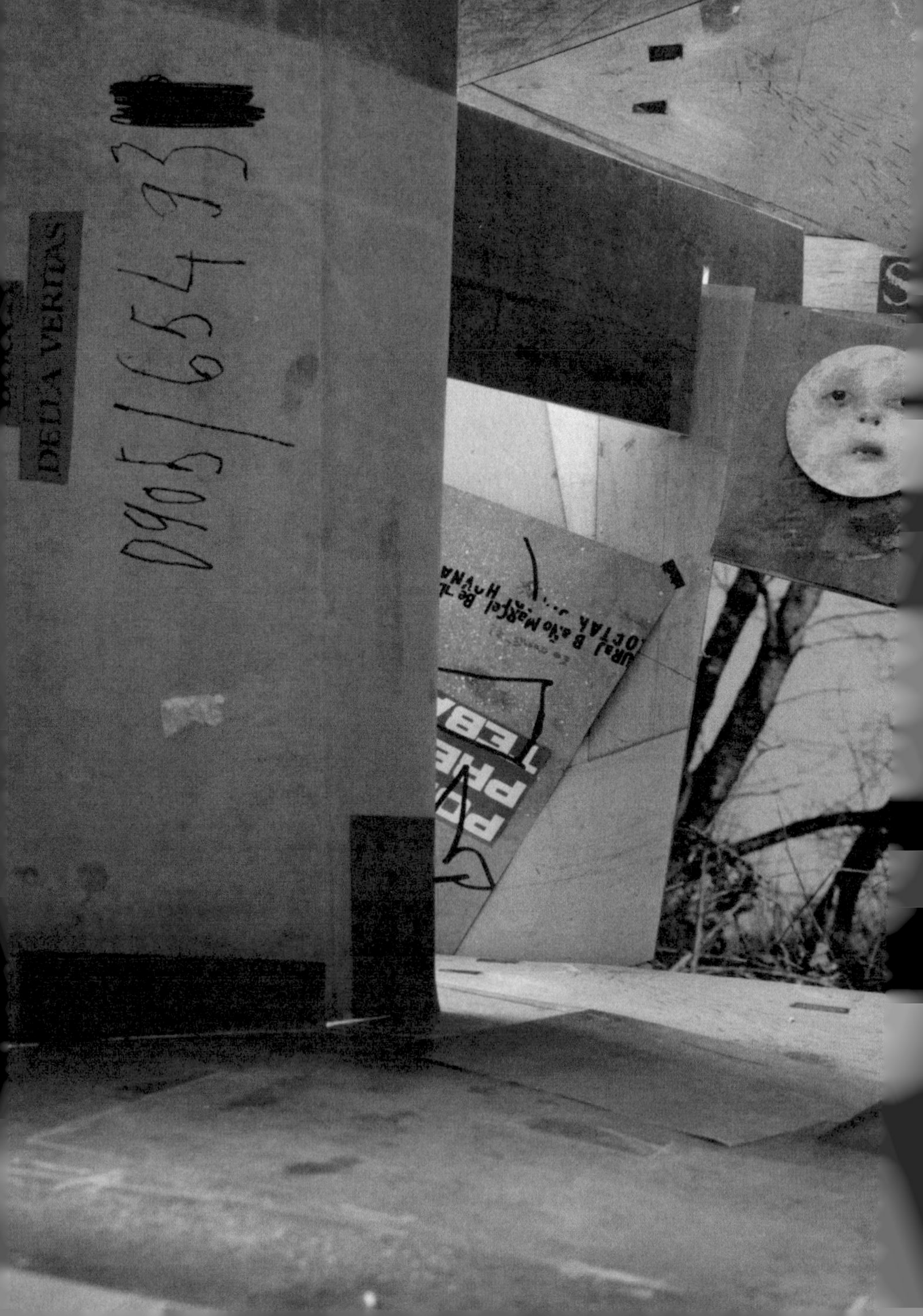

ARA BYSTRICA

BOCCA
DELLA VERITAS

555.000 €

Bocca
della
veritas

MILOŠ JE K!
KJEK!

MILOŠ

where nature turns to altered states

where mountains meets at twins
where rivers see the wooden gate
a different dream begins

Since then I never stopped

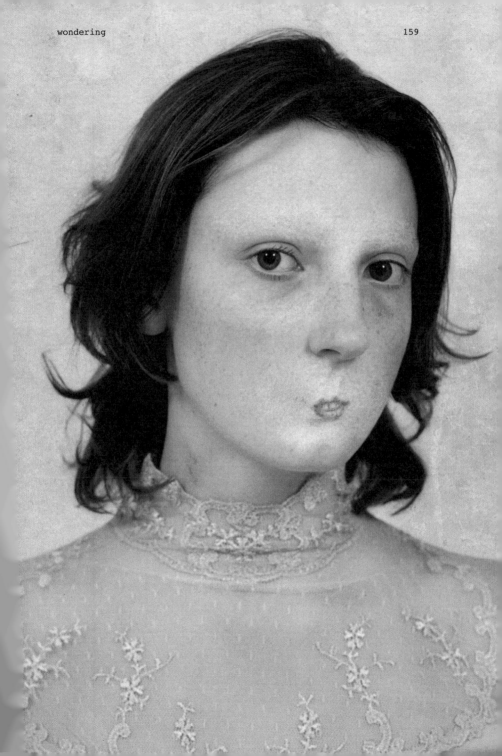

erter now the torture cell
and suffer stitching pain
what you are the mouth will tell
where you got the chain

high up the mountain

down in the well

deep in the forest

break up the spell

Phobias

---   –

A Human Confrontation with the
New Civilization

---   –

Edited by peach

The real and specific cause of phobias is often hard to identify.
Some are accompanied with frightening thoughts, others might
be associated with anxieties. They can also be defined as condi-
tioned (learned) anxiety response that has become associated
with a feared object. Some phobic events or attacks can cause
racing hearts, sweating, chest discomfort, trembling etc. In
worse cases these attacks can end up in hospital as sometimes
the aforementioned symptoms have similarities with e.g. heart
attacks. They certainly can interfere with the ability to live a
normal life.

According to the University of Cambridge Counselling Service «A phobia is an excessive or unreasonable fear of an object, place or situation. Phobias are extremely common. Sometimes they start in childhood for no apparent reason; sometimes they emerge after a traumatic event; and sometimes they develop from an attempt to make sense of an unexpected and intense anxiety or panic (e.g. ‹I feel fearful, therefore I must be afraid of something›).»[1]

In classic medical terms phobias are classified in six principal groups: Agoraphobia, Social phobia, Illness/Death phobias, Specific phobias, General/Diffuse phobic state and Obsessive/Compulsive disorders.[2]

Peach decided not to follow the classical categories of phobias. We tried to see it from the side of the vast multitudes of phobias. Therefore, this list is not necessarily categorized in its classic and medically acknowledged way.

It seems that phobias will keep science constantly busy. But as long as science is not willing to accept irrational and unexplainable motifs, illnesses such as phobias will remain a mystery. A mystery that can happen to anyone.

1) University of Cambridge Counselling Service 1998 (update 12/05/03) www.counselling.cam.ac.uk/phob.html

2) Steve Bremer © Miller Freeman UK Ltd www.dotpharmacy.co.uk/upphobia.html

BIOLOGICAL (FAUNA & FLORA)

Agrizoophobia	Fear of wild animals.
Ailurophobia	Fear of cats.
Alektorophobia	Fear of chicken.
Arachnophobia	Fear of spiders.
Anthrophobia or	
Anthophobia	Fear of flowers.
Apiphobia	Fear of bees.
Bacillophobia	Fear of microbes.
Bacteriophobia	Fear of bacteria.
Batrachophobia	Fear of amphibians, such as frogs, newts, salamanders, etc.
Botanophobia	Fear of plants.
Cynophobia	Fear of dogs or rabies.
Doraphobia	Fear of fur or skins of animals.
Dromophobia	Fear of crossing streets.
Elurophobia	Fear of cats.
Entomophobia	Fear of insects.
Equinophobia	Fear of horses.
Felinophobia or	
Galeophobia or	
Gatophobia	Fear of cats.
Herpetophobia	Fear of reptiles or creepy, crawly things.
Hippophobia	Fear of horses.
Ichthyophobia	Fear of fish.
Insectophobia	Fear of insects.
Isopterophobia	Fear of termites, insects that eat wood.
Lutraphobia	Fear of otters.
Melissophobia	Fear of bees.
Microbiophobia	Fear of microbes.
Mottephobia	Fear of moths.
Musophobia or	
Muriphobia	Fear of mice.
Myrmecophobia	Fear of ants.
Ophidiophobia	Fear of snakes
Ornithophobia	Fear of birds.
Ostraconophobia	Fear of shellfish.
Pediculophobia or	
Phthiriophobia	Fear of lice.
Ranidaphobia	Fear of frogs.
Scoleciphobia	Fear of worms.
Selachophobia	Fear of sharks.
Snakephobia	Fear of snakes.
Spheksophobia	Fear of wasps.
Suriphobia	Fear of mice.
Taurophobia	Fear of bulls.
Zemmiphobia	Fear of the great mole rat.
Zoophobia	Fear of animals.

COLORS

Chromophobia or	
Chromatophobia	Fear of colors.
Erythrophobia or	
Erytophobia or	
Ereuthophobia	Fear of redlights or blushing or red.
Leukophobia	Fear of color white.
Melanophobia	Fear of color black.
Porphyrophobia	Fear of color purple.
Xanthophobia	Fear of color yellow or the word yellow.

CHEMICALS

Toxiphobia	Fear of poison or of being accidently poisoned.

DOMESTIC

Amathophobia	Fear of dust.
Ataxophobia	Fear of disorder or untidiness.
Domatophobia	Fear of houses or being in a house.
Ecophobia	Fear of home surroundings.
Mageirocophobia	Fear of cooking.
Nostophobia	Fear of returning home.
Oikophobia	Fear of home surroundings, houses.

ETHNIC / POLITICAL / PROFESSIONS

Anglophobia	Fear of England or English culture.
Bolshephobia	Fear of Bolsheviks.
Coulrophobia	Fear of clowns.
Cypridophobia or	
Cypriphobia or	
Cyprinophobia	Fear of prostitutes or venereal disease.
Demonophobia or	
Daemonophobia	Fear of demons.
Dentophobia	Fear of dentists.
Dutchphobia	Fear of the Dutch.
Francophobia or	
Gallophobia or	
Galiophobia	Fear of France.

Germanophobia	Fear of Germany or German culture.
Gerontophobia	Fear of old people or of growing old.
Hierophobia	Fear of priests or sacred things.
Hobophobia	Fear of bums or beggars.
Homilophobia	Fear of sermons.
Japanophobia	Fear of Japanese.
Judeophobia	Fear of Jews.
Papaphobia	Fear of the Pope.
Philosophobia	Fear of philosophy.
Politicophobia	Fear or abnormal dislike of politicians.
Russophobia	Fear of Russians.
Sinophobia	Fear of Chinese or Chinese culture.
Teutophobia	Fear of Germany or German things.
Theologicophobia	Fear of theology.
Theophobia	Fear of gods or religion.
Xenoglossophobia	Fear of foreign languages.
Xenophobia	Fear of strangers or foreigners.
Zeusophobia	Fear of God or gods.

FOODS / NUTRIENTS

Alliumphobia	Fear of garlic.
Arachibutyro-phobia	Fear of peanut butter sticking to the roof of the mouth.
Lachanophobia	Fear of vegetables.
Oenophobia	Fear of wines.
Sitophobia or Sitiophobia	Fear of food or eating.

INTIMATE / SEXUAL

Ablutophobia	Fear of washing or bathing.
Acarophobia	Fear of itching or of the insects that cause itching.
Agraphobia	Fear of sexual abuse.
Anuptaphobia	Fear of staying single.
Athazagoraphobia	Fear of being forgotten or ignored or forgetting.
Atychiphobia	Fear of failure.
Autodysomophobia	Fear of one that has a vile odor.

Automysophobia	Fear of being dirty.
Bromidrosiphobia or Bromidrophobia	Fear of body smells.
Cacophobia	Fear of ugliness.
Clinophobia	Fear of going to bed.
Coitophobia	Fear of coitus.
Contreltophobia	Fear of sexual abuse.
Decidophobia	Fear of making decisions.
Dipsophobia	Fear of drinking.
Dishabiliophobia	Fear of undressing in front of someone.
Erotophobia	Fear of sexual love or sexual questions.
Eurotophobia	Fear of female genitalia.
Genophobia	Fear of sex.
Gymnophobia	Fear of nudity.
Haphephobia or Haptephobia	Fear of being touched.
Hypnophobia	Fear of sleep or of being hypnotized.
Iatrophobia	Fear of going to the doctor or of doctors.
Ithyphallophobia	Fear of seeing, thinking about or having an erect penis.
Kathisophobia	Fear of sitting down.
Malaxophobia	Fear of love play.
Medomalacuphobia	Fear of losing an erection.
Medorthophobia	Fear of an erect penis.
Nudophobia	Fear of nudity.
Oneirophobia	Fear of dreams.
Oneirogmophobia	Fear of wet dreams.
Osmophobia	Fear of smells or odors.
Paraphobia	Fear of sexual perversion.
Pathophobia	Fear of disease.
Phallophobia	Fear of a penis, especially erect.
Philemaphobia or Philematophobia	Fear of kissing.
Sarmassophobia	Fear of love play.
Sexophobia	Fear of the opposite sex.
Virginitiphobia	Fear of rape.

MENTAL

Acerophobia	Fear of sourness.
Achluophobia	Fear of darkness.
Acousticophobia	Fear of noise.
Aviophobia or Aviatophobia	Fear of flying.
Agateophobia	Fear of insanity.
Algophobia	Fear of pain.
Ambulophobia	Fear of walking.
Amnesiphobia	Fear of amnesia.

Anablephobia	Fear of looking up.	Hypsiphobia	Fear of height.
Apeirophobia	Fear of infinity.	Illyngophobia	Fear of vertigo or
Asthenophobia	Fear of fainting or		feeling dizzy when
	weakness.		looking down.
Asymmetriphobia	Fear of asymmetrical	Kinetophobia or	
	things.	Kinesophobia	Fear of movement or
Atelophobia	Fear of imperfection.		motion.
Atomosophobia	Fear of atomic	Logophobia	Fear of words.
	explosions.	Lygophobia	Fear of darkness.
Cainophobia or		Lyssophobia	Fear of rabies or of
Cainotophobia	Fear of newness, novelty.		becoming mad.
Cenophobia or		Maniaphobia	Fear of insanity.
Centophobia	Fear of new things	Mastigophobia	Fear of punishment.
	or ideas.	Metathesiophobia	Fear of changes.
Chronophobia	Fear of time.	Mnemophobia	Fear of memories.
Clithrophobia or		Myctophobia	Fear of darkness.
Cleithrophobia	Fear of being enclosed.	Onomatophobia	Fear of hearing a cer-
Counterphobia	The preference by a		tain word or of names.
	phobic for fearful	Optophobia	Fear of opening one's
	situations.		eyes.
Dementophobia	Fear of insanity.	Philophobia	Fear of falling in love
Dextrophobia	Fear of objects at the		or being in love.
	right side of the body.	Polyphobia	Fear of many things.
Dinophobia	Fear of dizziness or	Prosophobia	Fear of progress.
	whirlpools.	Psychophobia	Fear of mind.
Diplophobia	Fear of double vision.	Pteromerhano-	
Dystychiphobia	Fear of accidents.	phobia	Fear of flying.
Eisoptrophobia	Fear of mirrors or of	Rhabdophobia	Fear of being severely
	seeing oneself in a		punished or beaten by
	mirror.		a rod, or of being
Enosiophobia or			severely criticized. Also
Enissophobia	Fear of having		fear of magic (wand).
	committed an	Scelerophibia	Fear of bad men,
	unpardonable sin or		burglars.
	fear of criticism.	Scriptophobia	Fear of writing in public.
Epistemophobia	Fear of knowledge.	Sesquipedalophobia	Fear of long words.
Euphobia	Fear of hearing good	Sinistrophobia	Fear of things to the
	news.		left or left handed.
Erythrophobia or		Somniphobia	Fear of sleep.
Erytophobia or		Sophophobia	Fear of learning.
Ereuthophobia	Fear of redlights	Taphephobia or	
	or blushing or red.	Taphophobia	Fear of being buried
Graphophobia	Fear of writing or		alive or of cemeteries.
	handwriting.	Tapinophobia	Fear of being contagious.
Hedonophobia	Fear of feeling pleasure.	Testophobia	Fear of taking tests.
Hellenologophobia	Fear of Greek terms	Thanatophobia or	
	or complex scientific	Thantophobia	Fear of death or dying.
	terminology.	Tropophobia	Fear of moving or
Heresyphobia or			making changes.
Hereiophobia	Fear of challenges to	Verbophobia	Fear of words.
	official doctrine or of	Zelophobia	Fear of jealousy.
	radical deviation.		
Hippopotomon-			
strosesquippedalio-			
phobia	Fear of long words.		
Hodophobia	Fear of road travel.		

NATURE AND NATURE RELATED PHENOMENONS

Ancraophobia or	
Anemophobia	Fear of wind.
Antlophobia	Fear of floods.
Arsonphobia	Fear of fire.
Astraphobia or	
Astrapophobia	Fear of thunder and lightning.
Astrophobia	Fear of stars or celestial space.
Aurophobia	Fear of gold.
Auroraphobia	Fear of Northern lights.
Brontophobia	Fear of thunder and lightning.
Carnophobia	Fear of meat.
Ceraunophobia	Fear of thunder and lightning.
Chionophobia	Fear of snow.
Coprophobia	Fear of feces.
Cymophobia	Fear of waves or wave like motions.
Dendrophobia	Fear of trees.
Cometophobia	Fear of comets.
Eosophobia	Fear of dawn or daylight.
Heliophobia	Fear of the sun.
Homichlophobia	Fear of fog.
Hydrophobia	Fear of water or of rabies.
Hylophobia	Fear of forests.
Keraunophobia	Fear of thunder and lightning.
Kosmikophobia	Fear of cosmic phenomenon.
Kymophobia	Fear of waves.
Lilapsophobia	Fear of tornadoes and hurricanes.
Limnophobia	Fear of lakes.
Meteorophobia	Fear of meteors.
Mycophobia	Fear or aversion to mushrooms.
Nebulaphobia	Fear of fog.
Necrophobia	Fear of death or dead things.
Noctiphobia	Fear of the night.
Nyctohylophobia	Fear of dark wooded areas or forests at night.
Nyctophobia	Fear of the dark or of night.
Olfactophobia	Fear of smells.
Ombrophobia	Fear of rain or of being rained on.
Ouranophobia or	
Pagophobia	Fear of ice or frost.

Phengophobia	Fear of daylight or sunshine.
Photoaugliaphobia	Fear of glaring lights.
Photophobia	Fear of light.
Pluviophobia	Fear of rain or of being rained on.
Potamophobia	Fear of rivers or running water.
Psychrophobia	Fear of cold.
Pyrophobia	Fear of fire.
Sciophobia or	
Sciaphobia	Fear of shadows.
Scotophobia	Fear of darkness.
Selaphobia	Fear of light flashes.
Selenophobia	Fear of the moon.
Seplophobia	Fear of decaying matter.
Siderophobia	Fear of stars.
Spacephobia	Fear of outer space.
Thalassophobia	Fear of the sea.
Thermophobia	Fear of heat.
Tonitrophobia	Fear of thunder.
Uranophobia	Fear of heaven.

NUMBERS

Arithmophobia	Fear of numbers.
Numerophobia	Fear of numbers.
Octophobia	Fear of the figure 8.
Triskaidekaphobia	Fear of the number 13.

TANGIBLES (OBJECTS, LIQUIDS) / TECHNOLOGY

Aichmophobia	Fear of needles or pointed objects.
Automatonophobia	Fear of ventriloquist's dummies, animatronic creatures, wax statues; anything that falsly represents a sentient being.
Ballistophobia	Fear of missiles or bullets.
Bibliophobia	Fear of books.
Blennophobia	Fear of slime.
Catoptrophobia	Fear of mirrors.
Chemophobia	Fear of chemicals or working with chemicals.
Chrometophobia or	
Chrematophobia	Fear of money.
Chronomentro-	
phobia	Fear of clocks.
Cibophobia	Fear of food.

Crystallophobia	Fear of crystals or glass.
Cyberphobia	Fear of computers or working on a computer.
Cyclophobia	Fear of bicycles.
Electrophobia	Fear of electricity.
Enetophobia	Fear of pins.
Hoplophobia	Fear of firearms.
Hyelophobia or Hyalophobia	Fear of glass.
Hygrophobia	Fear of liquids, dampness or moisture.
Hylephobia	Fear of materialism or the fear of epilepsy.
Iophobia	Fear of poison.
Linonophobia	Fear of strings.
Logizomechano-phobia	Fear of computers.
Mechanophobia	Fear of machines.
Megalophobia	Fear of large things.
Metallophobia	Fear of metal.
Methyphobia	Fear of alcohol.
Microphobia	Fear of small things.
Motorphobia	Fear of automobiles.
Myxophobia	Fear of slime.
Nelophobia	Fear of glass.
Nucleomituphobia	Fear of nuclear weapons.
Ochophobia	Fear of vehicles.
Orthophobia	Fear of property.
Papyrophobia	Fear of paper.
Pediophobia	Fear of dolls.
Pharmacophobia	Fear of drugs.
Placophobia	Fear of tombstones.
Potophobia	Fear of alcohol.
Pupaphobia	Fear of puppets.
Radiophobia	Fear of radiation, x-rays.
Rupophobia	Fear of dirt.
Siderodromophobia	Fear of trains, railroads or train travel.
Sitophobia or Sitiophobia	Fear of food.
Staurophobia	Fear of crosses or the crucifix.
Technophobia	Fear of technology.
Telephonophobia	Fear of telephones.
Textophobia	Fear of certain fabrics.
Vestiphobia	Fear of clothing.
Xylophobia	Fear of wooden objects or forests.
Xyrophobia	Fear of razors.

PHYSICAL / HEALTH RELATED

Aerophobia	Fear of drafts, air swallowing, or airbourne noxious substances.
Aeronausiphobia	Fear of vomiting secondary to airsickness.
Agliophobia	Fear of pain.
Aichmophobia	Fear of pins and needles.
Albuminurophobia	Fear of kidney disease.
Amathophobia	Fear of dust.
Amychophobia	Fear of scratches or being scratched.
Anemophobia or Ancraophobia	Fear of air drafts or wind.
Anginophobia	Fear of angina, choking or narrowness.
Ankylophobia	Fear of immobility of a joint.
Aphenphosmphobia	Fear of being touched.
Ataxiophobia	Fear of ataxia (muscular incoordination).
Barophobia	Fear of gravity.
Basophobia or Basiphobia	Inability to stand. Fear of walking or falling.
Belonephobia	Fear of pins and needles.
Cancerophobia or Carcinophobia	Fear of cancer.
Cardiophobia	Fear of the heart.
Cathisophobia	Fear of sitting.
Chaetophobia	Fear of hair.
Cheimaphobia or Cheimatophobia	Fear of cold.
Chiraptophobia	Fear of being touched.
Chirophobia	Fear of hands.
Chorophobia	Fear of dancing.
Cleptophobia	Fear of stealing.
Cnidophobia	Fear of stings.
Coprastasophobia	Fear of constipation.
Cryophobia	Fear of extreme cold, ice or frost.
Cypridophobia	Fear of venereal disease.
Defecaloesiophobia	Fear of painful bowels movements.
Dermatophobia	Fear of skin lesions.
Dermatosiophobia or Dermatophobia or Dermato-pathophobia	Fear of skin disease.
Diabetophobia	Fear of diabetes.
Dysmorphophobia	Fear of deformity.
Emetophobia	Fear of vomiting.
Epistaxiophobia	Fear of nosebleeds.

Febriphobia or	
Fibriphobia or	
Fibriophobia	Fear of fever.
Frigophobia	Fear of cold or cold things.
Geniophobia	Fear of chins.
Genuphobia	Fear of knees.
Gerascophobia	Fear of growing old.
Geumaphobia or	
Geumophobia	Fear of taste.
Haphephobia	Fear of being touched.
Helminthophobia	Fear of being infested with worms.
Hemophobia or	
Hemaphobia or	
Hematophobia	Fear of blood.
Hormephobia	Fear of shock.
Hydrargyophobia	Fear of mercurial medicines.
Hydrophobophobia	Fear of rabies.
Kolpophobia	Fear of genitals, particularly female.
Kopophobia	Fear of fatigue.
Koniophobia	Fear of dust.
Kleptophobia	Fear of stealing.
Kynophobia	Fear of rabies.
Kyphophobia	Fear of stooping.
Leprophobia or	
Lepraphobia	Fear of leprosy.
Levophobia	Fear of things to the left side of the body.
Ligyrophobia	Fear of loud noises.
Luiphobia	Fear of lues, syphilis.
Lyssophobia	Fear of rabies or of becoming mad.
Lockiophobia or	
Maieusiophobia	Fear of childbirth.
Meningitophobia	Fear of brain disease.
Menophobia	Fear of menstruation.
Merinthophobia	Fear of being bound or tied up.
Misophobia or	
Mysophobia	Fear of being contaminated with dirt or germs.
Molysmophobia or	
Molysomophobia	Fear of dirt or contamination.
Monopathophobia	Fear of definite disease.
Neopharmaphobia	Fear of new drugs.
Nosophobia or	
Nosemaphobia	Fear of becoming ill.
Obesophobia	Fear of gaining weight.
Odontophobia	Fear of teeth or dental surgery.
Odynophobia or	
Odynephobia	Fear of pain.

Ommetaphobia or	
Ommatophobia	Fear of eyes.
Opiophobia	Fear medical doctors experience of prescribing needed pain medications for patients.
Panthophobia	Fear of suffering and disease.
Parasitophobia	Fear of parasites.
Parturiphobia	Fear of childbirth.
Phagophobia	Fear of swallowing or of eating or of being eaten.
Phalacrophobia	Fear of becoming bald.
Pharmacophobia	Fear of taking medicine.
Phthisiophobia	Fear of tuberculosis.
Pnigophobia or	
Pnigerophobia	Fear of choking or of being smothered.
Pocrescophobia	Fear of gaining weight.
Pogonophobia	Fear of beards.
Poliosophobia	Fear of contracting poliomyelitis.
Proctophobia	Fear of rectums.
Psychrophobia	Fear of cold.
Pteronophobia	Fear of being tickled by feathers.
Pyrexiophobia	Fear of fever.
Rectophobia	Fear of rectum or rectal diseases.
Rhypophobia	Fear of defecation.
Rhytiphobia	Fear of getting wrinkles.
Scabiophobia	Fear of scabies.
Scatophobia	Fear of fecal matter.
Scotomaphobia	Fear of blindness in visual field.
Spermatophobia or	
Spermophobia	Fear of sperm or germs.
Stasibasiphobia	
or Stasiphobia	Fear of standing or walking.
Syphilophobia	Fear of syphilis.
Taeniophobia or	
Teniophobia	Fear of tapeworms.
Teratophobia	Fear of bearing a deformed child or fear of monsters or deformed people.
Tetanophobia	Fear of lockjaw, tetanus.
Thaasophobia	Fear of sitting.
Tocophobia	Fear of pregnancy or childbirth.
Tomophobia	Fear of surgical operations.
Traumatophobia	Fear of injury.
Tremophobia	Fear of trembling.

Trichinophobia	Fear of trichinosis.
Trichopathophobia or Trichophobia	Fear of hair.
Trypanophobia	Fear of injections.
Tuberculophobia	Fear of tuberculosis.
Urophobia	Fear of urine or urinating.
Vaccinophobia	Fear of vaccination.
Verminophobia	Fear of germs.
Xerophobia	Fear of dryness.

PLACES

Acrophobia	Fear of heights.
Aeroacrophobia	Fear of open high places.
Agoraphobia	Fear of open spaces, being in crowded places or leaving a safe place.
Agyrophobia	Fear of streets or crossing the street.
Atephobia	Fear of ruin or ruins.
Altophobia	Fear of heights.
Amaxophobia	Fear of riding in a car.
Aulophobia	Fear of flutes.
Bathmophobia	Fear of stairs or steep slopes.
Bathophobia	Fear of depth.
Batophobia	Fear of heights or being close to high buildings.
Catapedaphobia	Fear of jumping from high and low places.
Claustrophobia	Fear of confined spaces.
Cleithrophobia or Cleisiophobia	Fear of being locked in an enclosed place.
Climacophobia	Fear of stairs, climbing, or of falling downstairs.
Cremnophobia	Fear of precipices.
Coimetrophobia	Fear of cemeteries.
Gephyrophobia or Gephydrophobia or Gephysrophobia	Fear of crossing bridges.
Kenophobia	Fear of voids or empty spaces.
Koinoniphobia	Fear of rooms.
Nosocomephobia	Fear of hospitals.
Stenophobia	Fear of narrow things or places.
Theatrophobia	Fear of theatres.
Topophobia	Fear of certain places or situations, such as stage fright.

SOCIAL

Agoraphobia	Fear of crowds.
Allodoxaphobia	Fear of opinions.
Androphobia	Fear of men.
Angrophobia	Fear of anger or of becoming angry.
Anthropophobia	Fear of people or society.
Apotemnophobia	Fear of persons with amputations.
Arrhenphobia	Fear of men.
Autophobia	Fear of being alone or of oneself.
Caligynephobia	Fear of beautiful women.
Catagelophobia	Fear of being ridiculed.
Cherophobia	Fear of gaiety.
Cholerophobia	Fear of anger or the fear of cholera.
Deipnophobia	Fear of dining or dinner conversations.
Demophobia	Fear of crowds.
Didaskaleinophobia	Fear of going to school.
Dikephobia	Fear of justice.
Doxophobia	Fear of expressing opinions or of receiving praise.
Ecclesiophobia	Fear of church.
Eleutherophobia	Fear of freedom.
Enochlophobia	Fear of crowds.
Ephebiphobia	Fear of teenagers.
Eremophobia	Fear of being oneself or of loneliness.
Ereuthrophobia	Fear of blushing.
Ergasiophobia	Fear of work or functioning or surgeon's fear of operating.
Ergophobia	Fear of work.
Gamophobia	Fear of marriage.
Geliophobia	Fear of laughter.
Glossophobia	Fear of speaking in public or of trying to speak.
Gnosiophobia	Fear of knowledge.
Gynephobia or Gynophobia	Fear of women.
Hadephobia	Fear of hell.
Hagiophobia	Fear of saints or holy things.
Hamartophobia	Fear of sinning.
Harpaxophobia	Fear of being robbed.
Heterophobia	Fear of the opposite sex.
Hominophobia	Fear of men.
Homophobia	Fear of sameness, monotony or of homosexuality or of becoming homosexual.

Hypengyophobia or	
Hypegiaphobia	Fear of responsibility.
Ideophobia	Fear of ideas.
Isolophobia	Fear of solitude, being alone.
Kainolophobia or	
Kainophobia	Fear of anything new or novelty.
Kakorrhaphio-phobia	Fear of failure or defeat.
Katagelophobia	Fear of ridicule.
Laliophobia or	
Lalophobia	Fear of speaking.
Liticaphobia	Fear of lawsuits.
Macrophobia	Fear of long waits.
Melophobia	Fear or hatred of music.
Metrophobia	Fear or hatred of poetry.
Monophobia	Fear of solitude or being alone.
Mythophobia	Fear of myths or stories or false statements.
Neophobia	Fear of anything new or novelty.
Nomatophobia	Fear of names.
Novercaphobia	Fear of your step mother.
Ochlophobia	Fear of crowds or mobs.
Ophthalmophobia	Fear of being stared at.
Panophobia or	
Pantophobia	Fear of everything.
Paralipophobia	Fear of neglecting duty or responsibility.
Parthenophobia	Fear of virgins or young girls.
Patroiophobia	Fear of heredity.
Peccatophobia	Fear of sinning or imaginary crimes.
Pedophobia	Fear of children.
Peladophobia	Fear of bald people.
Peniaphobia	Fear of poverty.
Pentheraphobia	Fear of mother in law.
Phobophobia	Fear of phobias.
Phonophobia	Fear of noises or voices or one's own voice or of telephones.
Phronemophobia	Fear of thinking.
Plutophobia	Fear of wealth.
Poinephobia	Fear of punishment.
Ponophobia	Fear of overworking or of pain.
Psellismophobia	Fear of stuttering.
Scolionophobia	Fear of school.
Scopophobia or	
Scoptophobia	Fear of being seen or stared at.
Sexophobia	Fear of the opposite sex.

Soceraphobia	Fear of parents in law.
Social Phobia	Fear of being evaluated negatively in social situations.
Sociophobia	Fear of society or people in general.
Soteriophobia	Fear of dependence on others.
Stygiophobia or	
Stigiophobia	Fear of hell.
Syngenesophobia	Fear of relatives.
Tyrannophobia	Fear of tyrants.
Venustraphobia	Fear of beautiful women.
Vitricophobia	Fear of your step father.

OCCULT

Bogyphobia	Fear of bogeys or the bogeyman.
Ouranophobia	Fear of heaven.
Paraskavedekatria-phobia	Fear of Friday the 13th.
Phasmophobia	Fear of ghosts.
Pneumatiphobia	Fear of spirits.
Samhainophobia	Fear of Halloween.
Satanophobia	Fear of Satan.
Spectrophobia	Fear of specters or ghosts.
Symbolophobia	Fear of symbolism.
Symmetrophobia	Fear of symmetry.
Teleophobia	Fear of definite plans or religious ceremony.
Uranophobia	Fear of heaven.
Wiccaphobia	Fear of witches and witchcraft.

In 1989 an SR-71 aircraft crashed

Chairs

---   -

By Nataliya Slinko

---   -

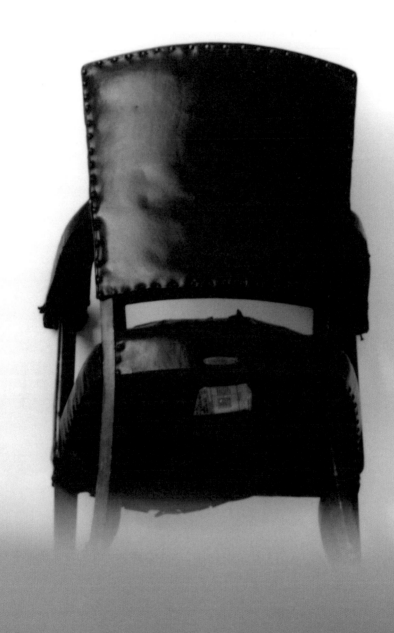

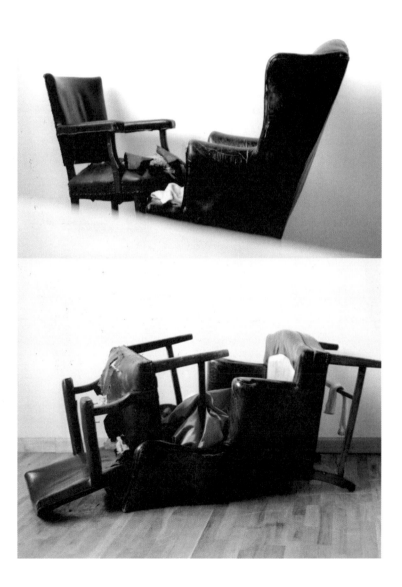

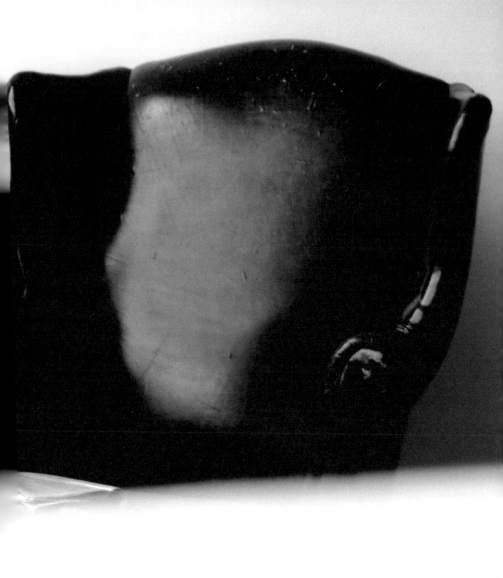

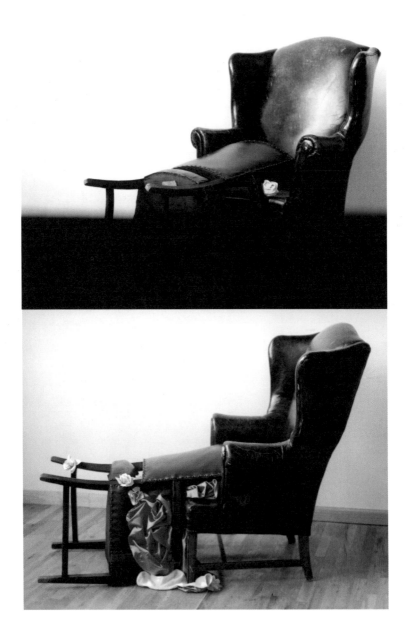

The Love Atlas

---   -

Artistic Research on the Physiognomy of Love Relations.

---   -

Installation by Tiziana Panizza with Photos by Liana Miuccio

The true mystery of the world is the visible not the invisible.
Oscar Wilde

Almost a Love Conference

You can't rush mysteries; it's better to let them settle in your heart while you stop and ponder each detail, without betraying what you feel. I remember very well the first mystery of my life, although at the time I was only a few months old.

It happened indoors, most probably during the day.

The scene was fuzzy then, and of course it still is. I remember more lights than objects, more sounds than words, and two faces. I buried myself in those two faces, spent hours and hours looking at them. Mouth, nose, eyes. The interest must have been mutual. Then, suddenly, the scene I've just described dramatically changed, and I will never forget it, even though I realize that when you tell the story it doesn't sound like much. The eyes trained on me cease to look at me and their gazes meet in a very special way. If I could explain it, I wouldn't be here, many years later, still trying to understand. At the time I had a body forty centimeters long, and a neuronal system with an amazing ability to form synapses, which unfortunately let me down when I was five, before I had the time to find an answer.

Which mystery bound the two smiling faces that—even before knowing their names—I knew belonged to my parents?

Years later I would learn that art, science, politics have been occupying themselves with love for millennia, and yet still have been unable to explain why we love one person and not another.

«There are lovers who spend their entire lives together without knowing what they want from each other. Each one's soul thirsts for something which no words exist to describe, and divines what it seeks, and traces obscurely the footsteps of its obscure desire,» says the Symposium.

This seemingly immaterial incident, which happened before I learned to read, made me an amazed witness to any love relationship.

Silvia & Sandro

44° 3' north   12° 34' east

Werner & Mona — 52° 30' north   13° 25' east
Abeba & Amdu — 90° 2' north   38° 45' east

Annalisa & Gigi — 45° 27' north 9° 11' east
David & Maya — 37° 2' north 38°45' east

I feel the same emotion every time I come into contact with a flesh-and-blood couple of lovers (I don't feel it at the cinema or when I read a novel or a poem). Real people in love give me a sense of subtle disquiet and optimism.

Disquiet because by a whisker they might have missed each other. «Centuries and centuries and facts only happen in the present,» wrote Borges. Or they don't happen at all. There's always some tiny thing that is enough to make something happen, some tiny thing that might prevent it happening. Eight years before meeting Yohannes I traveled to America for the first time, and among all possible cities I ended up in Boston. I could see his garden from the window and perhaps I even chanced to walk beside him on the pavement some day. Maybe my shopping bag unwittingly brushed against him, absentminded, I may have glanced at his shoes, our pheromones scattered in the air (I can't remember if at the time I used to wear a perfume, and which one it was). In addition to the time distance I've already mentioned, we were no less than 6589 kilometers from Rome, the place where we would finally cease to be two strangers.

I've adopted the belief of someone whose name I can't remember: the mysteries of love are to be found in the innumerable potential combinations of connections between people who love, which are also made up of intersections between cities, places, days, hours, weeks, years. Convinced of these connections, I've recently come to a decision: to discover what they are!

How? By creating an Atlas of people who love each other.

Every person who loves, like every life, is an encyclopaedia, a library, an inventory of reasons where everything can be reshuffled over and over, and rearranged in every possible way. Why not put all this together, in one collection? No love story can condense the mystery of all love stories, but perhaps their sum can. Mine, yours, theirs.

When our mind can't help us understand, we should abandon it. I'm not suggesting that we escape to dreams or to the irrational. In order to understand what the world hides, everything should be unravelled, organized, named with precision, described, located. Classifying is a process that can order, give meaning, provide an explanation, to something that is otherwise inexplicable.

In our case, we should bear in mind a caveat: In our Love Atlas we should classify lovers according to the rule of oneness: each of them is a unique specimen. I don't know you, so I don't know how you will feel about this proposal.

In my opinion the easiest way to collect and name what constitutes the uniqueness of each relationship and person is the picture of both. I know I'm asking a lot. What we say doesn't always resemble us, but the faces are real catchers of secrets. The number of possible human faces may exceed the number of subatomic particles in the universe. They sum up everything. Deep emotions and passions are revealed. They are the letters of an alphabet. A smile says, «all right,» a slight scowl, «forget it,» a certain stare, «I want it,» a nervous blink, «I don't believe you,» a dilation of the pupils, «have faith.» We are the only ones who know exactly what we feel. But it's the others who, while we are busy feeling, constantly have our faces before their eyes. We can't see what happens to our nose, our lips, our brow. They can. Everything is in the face, says Cicero.

Put your face in the Atlas. Put the face of the person you love as well. Put them close together and without knowing it you'll have many answers before your eyes. There's more. If you look closely, a net of invisible lines forms the weave of today, of tomorrow, of always and of never.

All this can also be left unread, you don't have to decipher it. It's enough to intently observe the dots that form the oval of the face until they disappear. Like seeing, the ability to not see can also be developed.

The mystery of the world sticks to everything, even love.

Bill & Lynne

41° 53' north   12° 28' east

Luciano & Simona — 44° 3' north 12° 34' east
Liana & Tom — 40° 77' north   73° 98' east

Chiara & Ennio — 35° 40' north 139° 45 east
Charles & Giuseppe — 41° 53' north 12° 28' east

Maya & Giulio

41° 53' north   12° 28' east

Yohannes & Tiziana

41° 53' north   12° 28' east

Sofie's World

---   -

By Sofie Moons

---   -

PLEASE

PLEA

feel free
to make
a selection

A
N
D

to ZOOM IN
OR
OUT

I HOPE

YOU

DO [TO ROSEBUD ♥♥♥]

Happy greetings

SOFIE MOONS ✳ MOONSTRAAT 8
2018 ANTWERPEN ✳ BELGIE

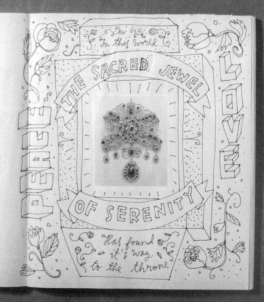

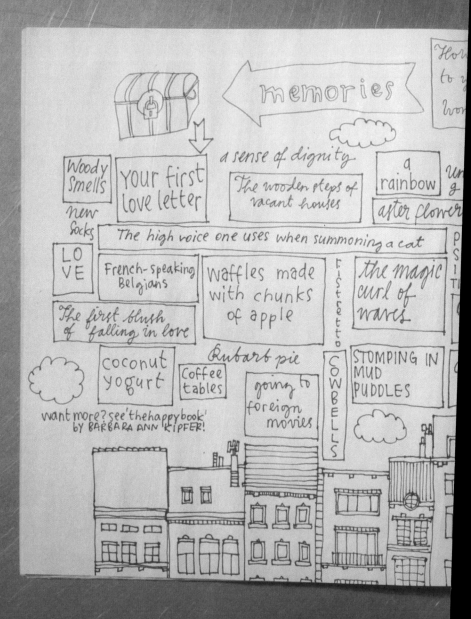

memories

a sense of dignity

Woody smells

your first love letter

The wooden steps of vacant houses

a rainbow

after flowers

new socks

The high voice one uses when summoning a cat

LOVE

French-speaking Belgians

Waffles made with chunks of apple

ristretto COWBELLS

the magic curl of waves

The first blush of falling in love

coconut yogurt

Rhubarb pie

Coffee tables

going to foreign movies

STOMPING IN MUD PUDDLES

want more? see 'the happy book' by BARBARA ANN KIPFER!

get
wn
nd

suivez les flèches svp.

imagination

Holi
days

a small fishing village

both
(les deux)

secondhand
compliments

Natural
Beauty

CARTE
BLANCHE

aycird
Falls

say
yes

Coney Island
hot dogs

enthu
siasm

HIRTS

country mist

a nice smell

andin

writing paper

close your eyes

LEAVE THIS
CITY

THE →
SANdbAR

SUMMER'S
READY
WHEN YOU are !

Thank you Sofie for your beautiful contribution.
We wish we could have shown all of it.

Modern Nursery Rhymes

By Jeffrey Lin

**Movements
don't die,
they just move.**

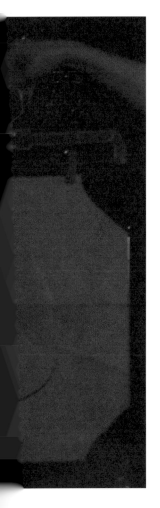

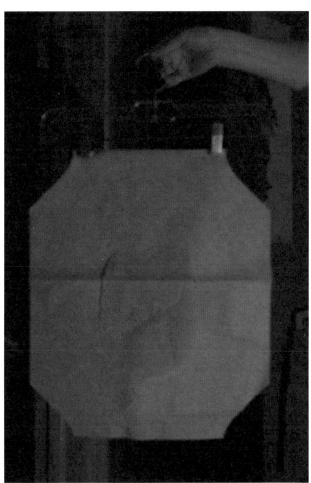

**Actually,
I prefer white.**

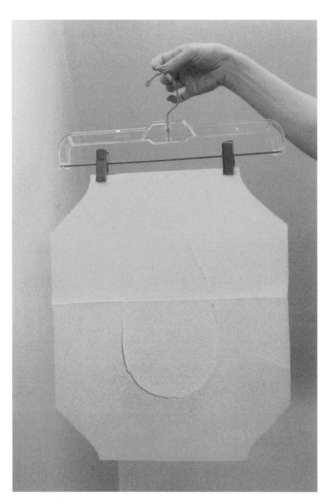

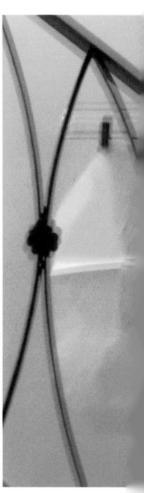

More of a
high note
than a low one.

There are simply
too many choices
in this upcoming
election.

Actually,
I heard that they will be carrying
a completely different line this spring.

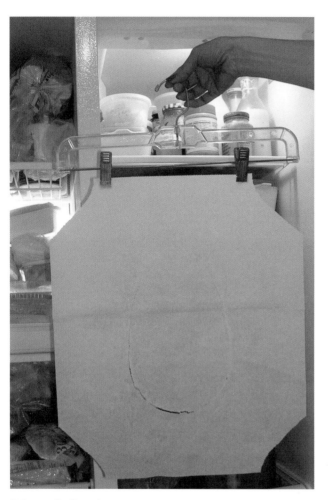

More of a licorice taste,
I'd say.

Absolutely
no problem at all.

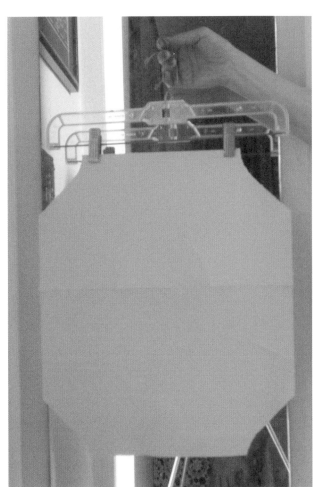

However.

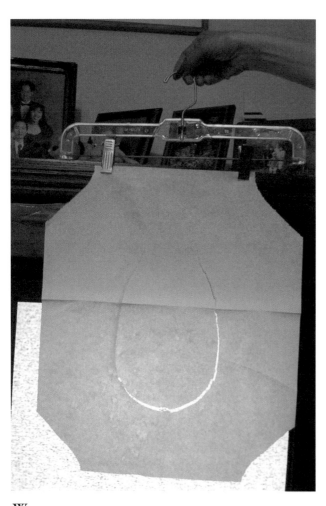

Wow,
I didn't know that
about your mom.

Well, somebody
has to pay
the bills around here

**How many times
do I have to tell you, turn off
the fucking television.**

**Salting and pickling were essential methods
of food preservation before they had refrigerators.**

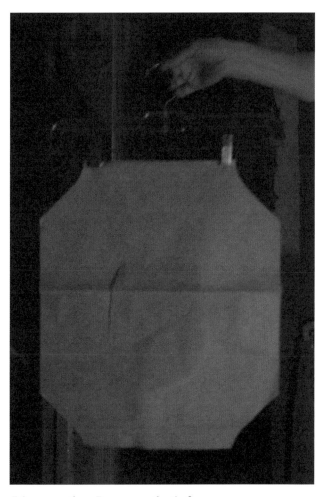

It's more than I can say, that's for sure.
What the hell is that?

Playroom Kids

---   -

By Sergio del Puerto

---   -

Been There — Great Place!

-

By Mark Glassner

-

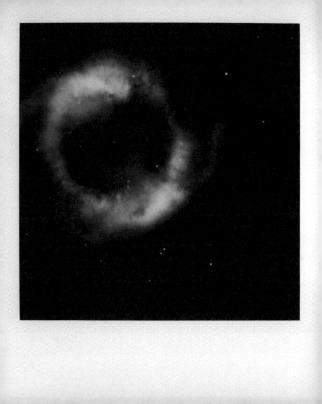

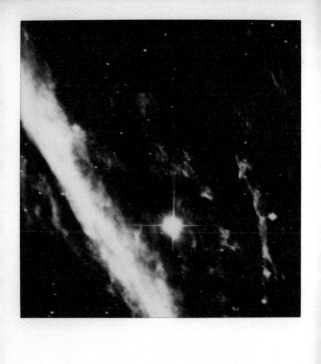

In Memory of Existence

\---

By Wolfgang Gosch

\---

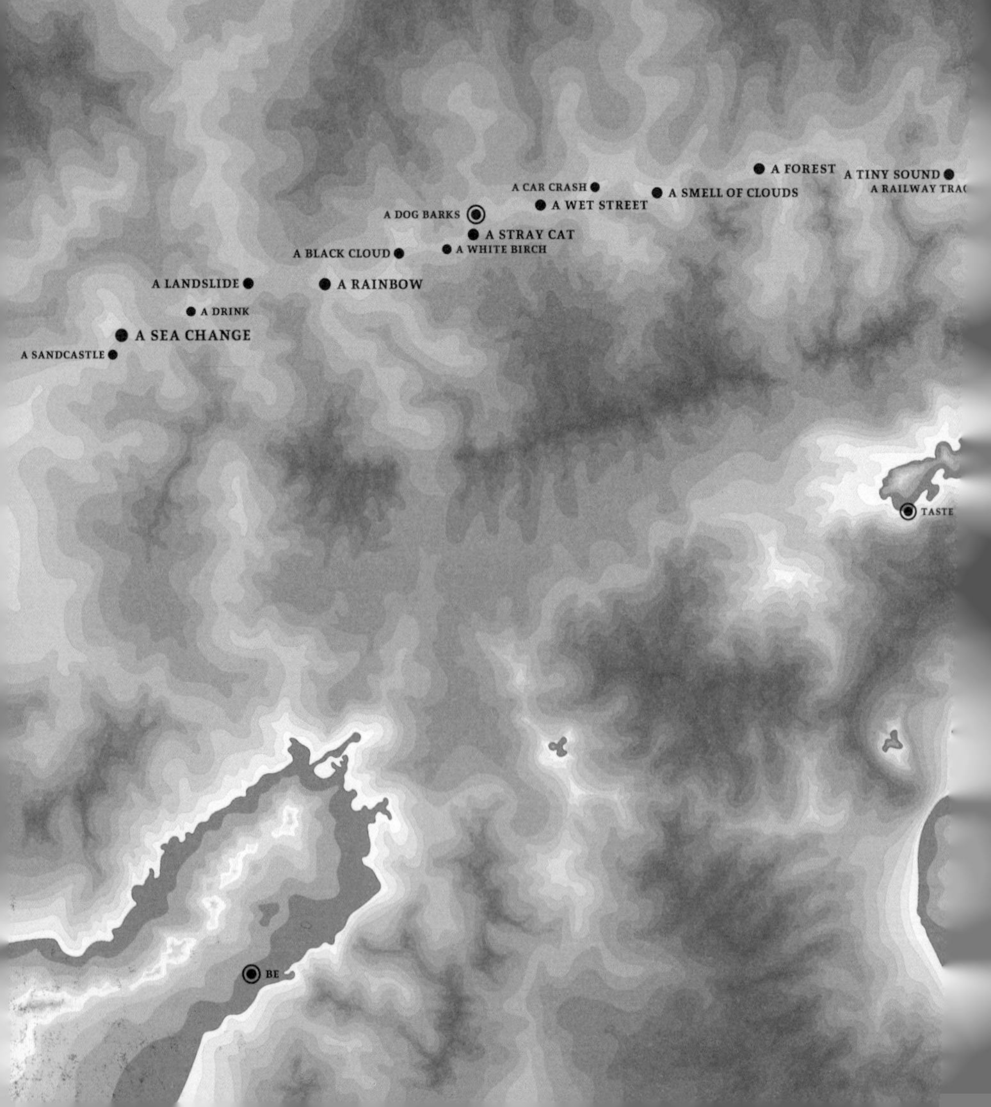

OFF TRACKS

● A FOREST

A TINY SOUND ●

A RAILWAY TRAC

A CAR CRASH ●

● A SMELL OF CLOUDS

A DOG BARKS ◉

A WET STREET

● A STRAY CAT

A BLACK CLOUD ●

● A WHITE BIRCH

A LANDSLIDE ●

● A RAINBOW

● A DRINK

● A SEA CHANGE

A SANDCASTLE ●

● TASTE

◉ BE

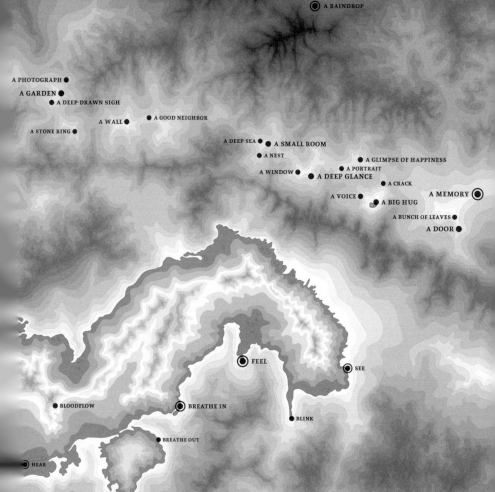

A LATERN ●
A RAY OF LIGHT ●

A GIRL ●
A SWEET WORD ●
A PLEASING SHIVER ●

A STAR MADE OF CARDBOARD ●

A RAINDROP ◉

A PHOTOGRAPH ●
A GARDEN ●
A DEEP-DRAWN SIGH ●
A GOOD NEIGHBOR ●
A WALL ●
A STONE RING ●

A DEEP SEA ● A SMALL ROOM ●
A NEST ●
A GLIMPSE OF HAPPINESS ●
A PORTRAIT ●
A WINDOW ● A DEEP GLANCE ●
A CRACK ●
A MEMORY ◉
A VOICE ● A BIG HUG ●
A BUNCH OF LEAVES ●
A DOOR ●

FEEL ◉
SEE ◉

BLOODFLOW ●
BREATHE IN ◉
BLINK ●

BREATHE OUT ●

HEAR ◉

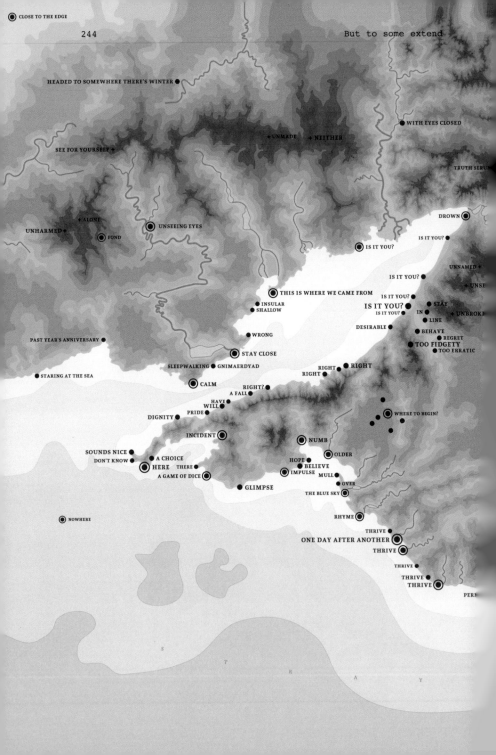

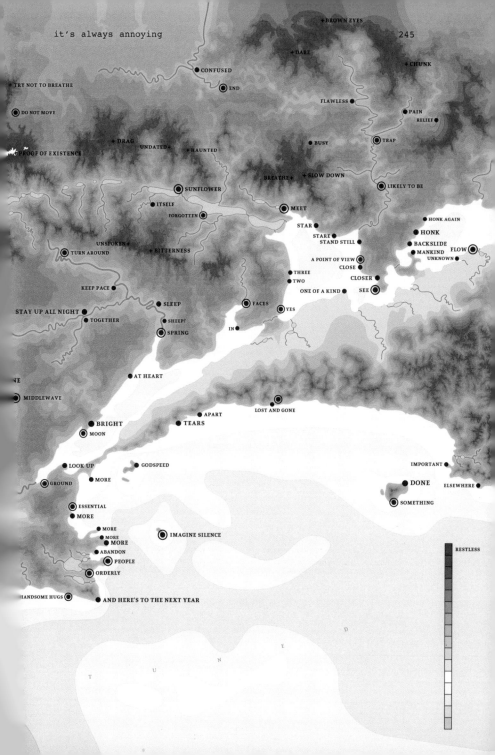

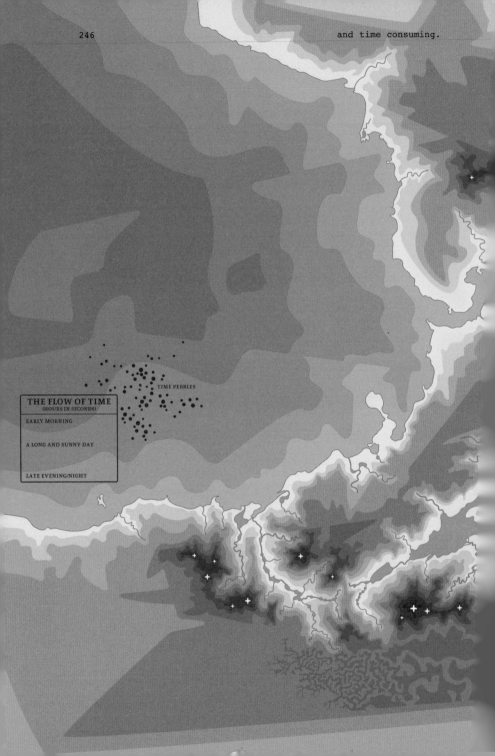

and time consuming.

THE FLOW OF TIME
(HOURS IN SECONDS)

EARLY MORNING

A LONG AND SUNNY DAY

LATE EVENING/NIGHT

TIME PEBBLES

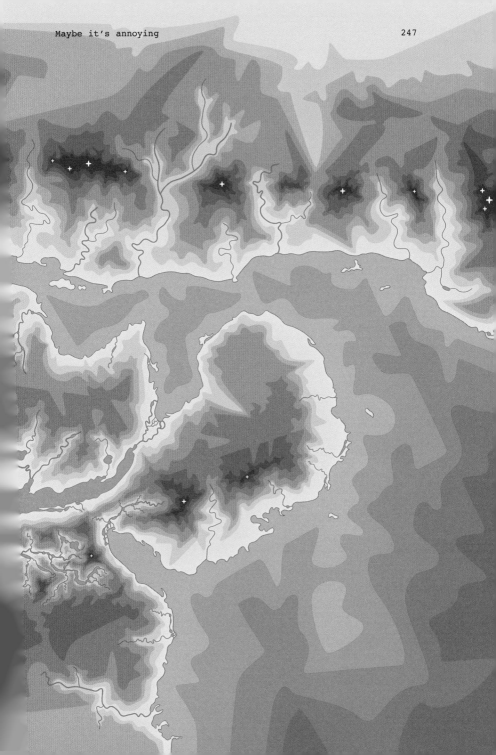

? A R E   W E   N O T   N O T   D R A W N   O N W A R D,   W E

HOW DOES
THE MORNING
TASTE?

AS A CHILD,
HOW DID YOU FEEL
STANDING OUTSIDE
IN THE SNOW COLD
PACKED IN
MOONBOOTS?

WHAT'S THE
COLOR OF THE SUN
WHEN YOU
LOOK AT IT WITH
CLOSED EYES?

WHAT KEEPS YOU
FROM TALKING TO
HER?

WHAT DOES THE
WORLD LOOK LIKE
WHEN YOU'RE NOT
WATCHING?

WHAT'S THE
WORLD BUT AN
ISLAND?

200   0   200   400   600

WHERE ARE YOU?

FEW DRAWN ONWARD TO NEW ERA

EVER KISSED
THE SUNLIGHT OFF
OF SNOWFLAKES?

WHAT IS BEHIND
THE LOOKING
GLASS?

EVER NOTICED
THE BEAUTIFUL
SOUND OF
CRACKING ICE
CUBES?

WHERE IS YOUR
SOUL WHILE YOU
SLEEP?

DO WE FEEL
LONELY WHEN
WE DREAM?

Picture Kleptomania

---   -

By Lorenzo Petrantoni

---   -

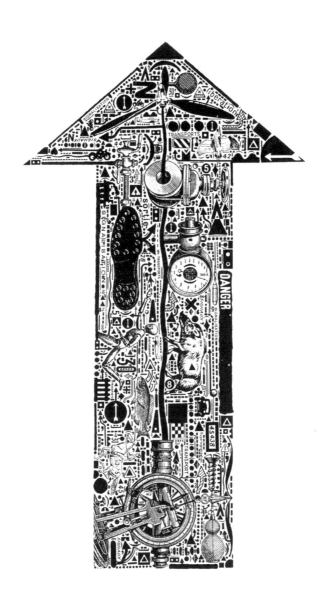

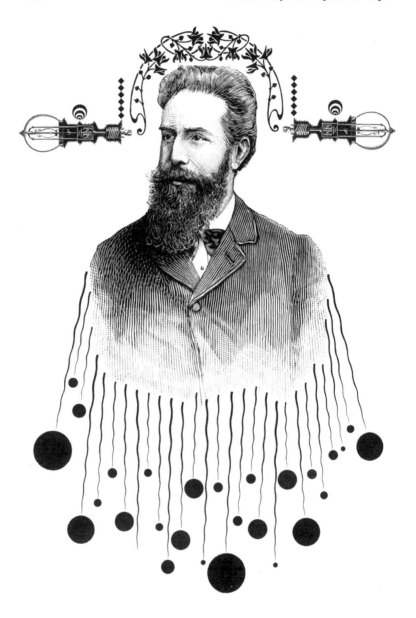

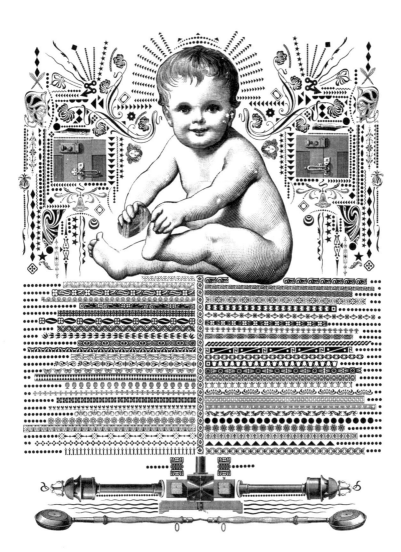

Maissonette Mousse

---   —

By Michael Dürr in Cooperation with Natalia Babska,
Martina Kröll, Mathias Meissl and Amra Rasidkadic

---   —

Monster Water

---   –

By Ernst Molden with Illustrations by Silja Götz

---   –

I. Newspaper Report

M.-See, Austria. Do the Alps have their Loch Ness now? At least
at M.-See in Austria, five witnesses saw the same incredible zoo-
logical phenomenon. At a tightly constricted part of the body of
water, according to the surprisingly similar eyewitness reports,
an animal of at least seven meters' length emerged from the water. It looked like a soft-shelled turtle with an extremely long,
flexible neck. The witnesses said that the animal made soft sounds
as it moved its neck in all different directions, before sinking
back into the water's current leaving an eddy in its wake.

The witnesses include the Catholic priest from the village
of M., and a seven-year-old child, who has been in a state of
shock since the experience.

In an initial statement, a biologist from the University of K.
who specializes in the animals of this particular lake, mentioned
the widely varying temperatures between the eastern part of
the lake and the much deeper western part. At the narrow sec-
tion in question, very often there were fog banks that reached
almost down to the water's surface. These could strongly distort
or enlarge real phenomena. The supposed monstrosity could be
a sort of fog hologram of a great crested grebe fishing nearby.

The zoologist added that in recent years a number of new
species had been discovered in M.-See. However, they were all
freshwater plankton, none of which were more than half a millimeter in size.

II. Statement of Witness A (Schoolchild, age 7)

WITNESS A: First I thought it was a boat. Or a paraglider that
had landed in the water nearby. The sound came from over
there, from the side where the people are. I went to the lake at a
place where nobody else was. I always go the same way. Straight
down. On top is the hunting lodge with the deer antlers, now
they call it administration center. In front is a parking area for
the lumber trucks, then there's a hedge, and behind the hedge
the woods begin, and this path. It goes right down the mountain, and at the very bottom there are a few rocks, then the
water. You can see the rocks from here.

Look, there's a narrow pass for the lumberjacks.

They used to take this way. That's what they told me.
They pulled the trees straight down to the water and then floated
them across the lake. On the other side, where the people are,
they built two villages. Now they have the parking area and the
trucks. The path is covered with rotten leaves. Smell. It always
stinks a bit. I don't want to swim. I just want to be by the water.

III. The Chronicler's Research

The lake's form has been compared to a short-legged dog. Very old chronicles refer to the seven-kilometer-long lake as Dogswater, before the founding of M. in 1345 gave it the name M.-See.

The dog's head looks to the west and forms the deeper but paradoxically warmer part of M.-See. The source of the warmth is a spring seventy meters under the surface that brings warm water into the lake. This influx and Schott Creek, which flows into the end of the dog's snout, fill the lake. The dog's head is the lonely part of the lake. Except for a couple of barely used fisherman's boat ramps and a logging campsite, it is surrounded by a forest of mountain maples and old firs. Almost a decade ago, the national forest service sold the woods to a German wood products company, which uses the timber from the mountain maples to make instruments, among other things.

The two settlements on the lake, M., which is smaller, and U., which is more extensive, partly as a result of summertime tourism, lie on the eastern, shallower basin. Tourism in the summer has developed since the nineteenth century, and in addition, at Easter the church in U. hosts a festival of sacred music. In the shallow valleys east of the lake there are three sailing and windsurfing schools, as well as some agriculture — mainly herds of dairy cows. On the south side of the lake, the landscape rises steeply to the heights of the Grenzkogel massif. The cows graze here in summer. M., a small market town, has 800 inhabitants. U., spread out along the road, has 2,400.

The place of the alleged appearance is the constricted point between the lake's two basins. It is also the site of deep currents in both directions. The lake, which is 1.2 kilometers wide at its broadest point, narrows to a needle's eye of just 40 meters.

ANKOGEL
3263

DACHSTEIN
2998

GROSSER BUCHSTEIN
2224

HOCHTOR
2372

HOCHSCHWAB
2270

ÖTSCHER
1892

SCHNEEBERG
2075

RAX
2009

REISALPE
1398

SCHÖPFL
800

ANNINGER
674

LEOPOLDSBERG
423

IV. Statement of Witness B (Priest, age 53)

CHRONICLER: And was it really seven meters? Reverend, was it seven?

WITNESS B: The size of what one sees is not what matters. The color matters, I believe, and the thickness. Of what one sees. I have seen a number of things, I have had revelations, have testified to mysteries and miracles, in the years before they sent me here. I believe I saw the most during my novitiate, in the Vienna Woods. In those years, one is in God's embrace. One hallucinates without interruption. Or else one really sees more than before and afterward put together. The Brothers of the Holy Cross. Among them was Father Angelus, who had not taken the higher orders. He was a carpenter for the monastery. He had been in Fatima, where he looked after several angels and St. Elizabeth. Since then, he has been able to see everything, guardian angels and the small, poisonous demons by the side of the road. It was very instructive to walk through the countryside with him. He asked me to take a gospel and read it aloud to him.

He didn't read very well, he said. I read the Sermon on the Mount, casting out devils, and the parable of the prodigal son, especially the last one, that was Father Angelus' favorite story. And in between he told me about everything that he saw, at the side of the road, in the trees, in the gutters of the city. On our way back to the monastery, I saw things as well. God's spiritual soldiers, fighting for good, and the struggles of His adversaries, who would certainly be crushed.

Angelus himself later saw the Mother of God many times in the Vienna Woods, and where he had seen her, he caused chapels and shrines to be built. Don't believe that he was without influence in this matter.

Pause.

Forgive me. That is not why you are here.

V. Statement of Witness C (Innkeeper, age 40)

My partner had been rowing. I was getting the fishing lines ready. Someone had told us that pike preyed in the current. We had no idea.

Suddenly he said, «Look out, we're sliding down!» And we really were. The water's surface was suddenly tilted, we were sliding down, westward, through the gorge and the forest hollow, toward the dog's head. Not fast, but enough to notice. And as we looked over, we saw how on the other side, in the forest hollow, it was going up again. You've got to imagine, water that's going up and down. You think about Moses and the people of Israel and the parting of the sea.

A dislocation. The boat was really pushed backwards, and my partner's face was completely pale. That's when we sense the others. All of a sudden we were in contact with them. With the priest, with the lady in her boathouse and the little boy in the woods on the other side. We knew they were there, and could sense us too. What happened there made exactly the same impression on all of us.

We almost went under. That's the truth. Then there was an awful lot of spray or fog. And then it... it opened up, right in front of us. The water. Just look at the gorge. There on the other side is a small, rocky cape.

Our boat was just about there, when that happened. The water around us was flat again, everything was still, and then not even ten meters away it went down steeply.

Where to? We didn't see where. We were too close to the water. We only saw the entrance to the tube.

VI. The Chronicler's Research

In the forest there are red deer and other kinds of deer, foxes, badgers and pine martins. According to the local forester, in autumn solitary bears migrate through. Rare predatory birds, such as Alpine crows and Alpine jackdaws, and even stone eagles, live in the S. Kogel massif. Plus, jays, night owls and barn owls nest in firs there. The wetlands at the east end of the lake are home to grass frogs and moor frogs, plus two types of asps. In some of the natural clearings on the S. Kogel and in the clear-cut areas in the maple forest nests of different kinds of vipers have been found. In the summer, the meadows on the lake's southern and eastern shores play host to a large number of butterfly species, some of which are usually found in more southerly climes.

The lake itself is home to catfish, carp, fingerlings, pike, perch and other small fish, mountain boar and crested boar in its tributaries, and in one particular stream, Schott Creek, crawfish.

Nobody has ever seen an animal bigger than a cow here.

Further, the witnesses with whom I have just spoken describe absolutely unusual perceptions, such as holes or rapid changes in the lake's water level, but none of them speak of a turtle-like creature.

After the incident, a number of the witnesses received medical attention. The local police chief made a report, which the press office of the state government passed along electronically to news agencies. This text is the first one that mentions an «animal.» Interfakt, the agency for popularizing science, and, in a follow up, the Frankfurt papers, took up the report and nursed a monster that, it seems, the state politicians gave birth to.

Nevertheless, I believe that something truly astonishing happened here, quite apart from such claims.

VIII. Statement of Witness A (Schoolchild)

On that day, I came down really quick. I ran, because I wanted to build something.

It was early in the morning. I didn't wait up at the forester's house until the nanny brought breakfast. I just went. I wanted to build a tree house, I even brought a hammer and some nails. My mommy was going to come four days later, and I wanted to have it finished by then. I had already picked out my tree. Some of the branches reach out over the water, we'll be right there, and then we can see it. But when I was down there, I remembered what I hadn't thought about. The timber that I wanted to nail to the tree was too heavy. Plus they were too long. I didn't bring a saw. Where could I get a saw, I thought. The lumberjacks sure won't trust me with one, because then the nanny would scream.

I was just thinking about where they kept their saws when the noise came.

It was a noise like when you drink apple juice from a straw and you get a bunch of air with it. A noise like that, but big. The next thing I saw was a hole in the lake, a big hole, bigger than most boats, right where the lake gets narrow. The noise got louder. I was right by the water, but then I ran back uphill, back to here, where we're standing right now. The noise, that sucking, got stronger, and then suddenly it was all gone. Everything was still. Then I turned around again. The hole was finished, like a tube, always going in another direction into the lake, like it was swinging around under water.

VIII. Statement of Witness B (Priest)

Our monster never goes away. It's not a reptile, and not any other kind of animal that you see with your eyes. In the name of the Father, the Son and the Holy Ghost. We are here.

The only statue of St. Coloman south of the Alps. Most of them stand in wooded areas and look toward the Danube valley, but no one really knows why. But the figure in this shrine stands here in the south and looks toward Trieste. It was built at the beginning of the seventeenth century, probably by a homesick traveling monk. I can understand that very well. I don't like to travel on water. I believe, even the Lord didn't like to walk on it. And was I not right? Didn't the door to the great denier open on the water? This hole...

CHRONICLER: Why do you think that the state government has turned your hole into a sibilant turtle?

PRIEST: What, don't you understand? You are staying in the Villa Monteverdi. Haven't you seen the men from the state government, when they come with their fawning courtiers to eat and drink? They are sinning with their whores, their brothers and sisters, their mothers and dogs. In their sin, invoke the true and the natural. They want to separate our state from the rest of the country. They want to play Robin Hood swim in the lake afterward. They are all crazy and they are evil.

The state government needs something just like that, an animal that raises its dirty head from a magical lake like ours, a monster, a protective spirit, a demon for their heads and their future coat of arms. These lousy fools will build a pilgrimage place for the friends of monsters, they will found a heathen fashion, that will break like a firestorm over my church.

IX. Statement of Witness A (Schoolchild)

The tube went through. Through everything. The lake, the earth, through the ocean on the other side of the world, out into space. On the inside of the tube it was like faces on a movie screen, they shivered, the faces of the woman and the men in the boat, the face of the priest, even your face.

Strange, isn't it? We didn't know each other yet. But your face wasn't strange to me. No more time passed there. Besides, it was cold and I...

(Voice is lost in tempest.)

CHRONICLER: Excuse me?

The End.

Untitled

---   -

By Ella Propella

---   -

H.S.R.

---   -

(Hormonal Seismographic Renderings)

---   -

By tonho/Quinta-feira

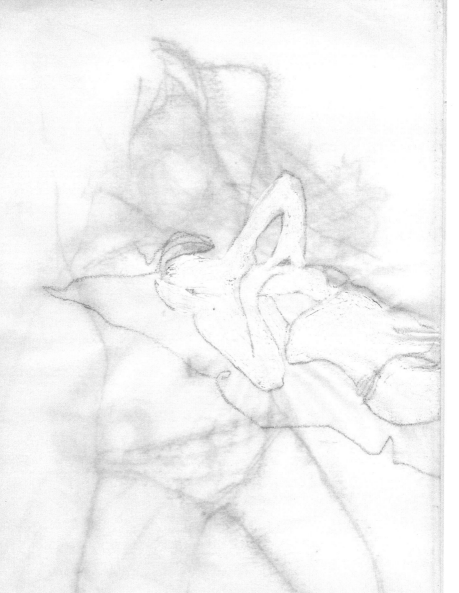

The idea of listening to the Mysteryland invitation in front of my computer just didn't feel right.

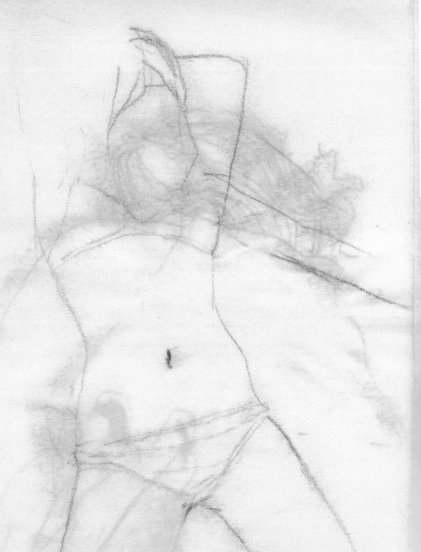

I decided to take my MP3-player to Reserva Beach, a protected area entirely free of any man-made constructions. Once there I felt a synesthetic sensation. The sublime relationship between image and spoken text.

My girlfriend lying on the sand, an invitation to transcend the over-rationalized regulatory world. The flow between thought and practise materializing.

I began to draw.

D

S

Brunnsteiner

---   -

By circus — Heidi Hackl and Andreas Schett

---   -

The contents of the present package were taken into
custody from the address Tiefer Graber 33, Top 2.
The apartment door was bolted, the sign on the door
gave no sign about the name of the occupant, and the
interior of the apartment also gave not the slightest
clue about the identity of the lessee who, according
to the neighbors' accounts, has been away since the
23rd of the month. Inquiries about the owner of the
apartment in question are underway. Fifteen of the
total of 17 pictures were made in the apartment that
the missing subject had recently inhabited.
This is shown beyond a shadow of a doubt by the
condition of the parquet floor. The carpet pictured
is a possession of the missing subject, the stain
covering approximately one-third of the carpet can be
ascribed to the drying of a large amount of water,
apparently melted ice.

MINE HOST S. C. ADAMS
Selecting Prime Steer Steaks

W   C

?   S

The apartment doorbell rang yet again; my spaghetti aglio e olio was just about ready. Pasta is always al dente, when I've got the razor on my chin.   The first time the doorbell rang this ~~morning~~, I was busy lathering up. Two ladies on the home stretch toward the change of life answering questions I never asked, Jehovah's Witnesses speaking in Catholic tongues, no thanks...

in other words, «Spit it out and swim home!» Just like the building super from my student days in Vienna used to say on such occasions. If you don't open the door for them, they trespass on your ears. They sing, loudly and penetratingly enough to fill the stairwell one of these new-fashioned hymns, M a n h a t t a n   T r a n s f e r for the congregation, or some such... How can anyone concentrate on shaving with that going in the background?

YOU HAVE UNDERSTOOD ME,

YOU KNOW WHO I AM.

And now it's ringing again. Another time swallower, another way of taking a bright morning and scrambling its otherwise perfect course. Taking a towel and quickly wiping the shaving cream off the face. For the unteachable, the old super from Vienna knew a very practical phrase, one that had so far sent everyone scurrying away, and one that I was thinking about using at impressive volume —

Naked male calves, shoes from B u d a p e s t and dark gray socks, the DHL delivery man in shorts and a blue and white striped shirt, «Your neighbor is not in right now, dear sir, would you mind accepting this package in his place?»

«I HAVE COME FROM AFAR AND WANT TO COME TO YOU,» sing the ladies from the first floor.

Brunnsteiner, of course Brunnsteiner is not to be found at eleven in the morning, Brunnsteiner is only there when he can annoy. Brunnsteiner leaves the building between eleven and two, because everyone knows that between eleven and two the radiation from the mobile phones is the strongest.

I never
step out of the door between eleven and two,
and you,   Mr. DHL,

you are always outside at exactly this time, and that in short
pants, but I can't take care of everything,
                                    hand it over...
                    The package was noticeably light, my food had
boiled away, the songs had gone next door. Now I could risk
going to the basement again, white clothes washed on the odd
days of the week, and on the way to the wash machine,
in front of the door to Brunnsteiner's apartment an unexpected
varnish of water, in which I naturally set my r i g h t f o o t .
Every step down the stairs pushed the wetness further and further through the felt soles of my house shoes, I left a one-legged
trail past the building's basement storage areas. I kicked angri-
ly at the threadbare red Persian carpet spread out in front of
Brunnsteiner's storage area.   Sabotage from a sense
of justice... with the success having my wet foot hurt as well, and
Brunnsteiner's carpet lying unchanged in the same place.
                    Brunnsteiner not only helped himself shamelessly to
my detergent, he also counted unapproved attachment of
P e r s i a n carpets to basement floors among his hobbies,
among the generally senseless activities that he pursued.

                    ~~The first time I saw him~~
            ~~was during the soccer World Cup last summer.~~

Twenty minutes before game time, he was marching proudly up
and down the street in a complete referee's uniform.
                                    This may be the right
time to mention that Brunnsteiner and I live on the ground
floor, and it was thus impossible for me to avoid the appearance
of referee Brunnsteiner. Just like Brunnsteiner in general, when
right in front of my eyes every day at dusk he strode to his tur-
quoise Opel Corsa, which he never drove, in which he only sat

U

T

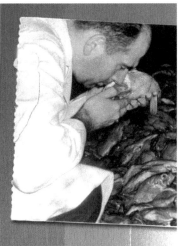

N   R

I

E

> «It's possible to imagine the world we live in like a house.
> There is a ground floor, an upper story, a cellar.
> But I am convinced that underneath the cellar, there is another cellar.
> If we really want to, we can enter it...»
> *Haruki Murakami*

> «Open no doors in this house!»
> *Elektra*

with an open passenger door and listened, at high volume, to the bird noises he had recorded earlier in the day —

　　　　The time until 2 p.m. is spent waiting for the wash to finish, animated movies and c o o k i n g programs on TV. Two o'clock. The day can begin. Stash Wittgenstein's book On Eroticism in the coat pocket, at five past enter Café Schwarzenbach and, as always, occupy the corner table next to the dumb waiter. ~~A large black coffee and a glass of water, which I pour into the cup. Coffee is always too hot and too strong. As usual, the Financial Times Germany is available.~~ I only ever open it to a particular page, the stock market, a world that I will never understand, but one that I belong to since the time that my obsessive sympathy for the Cape Verdes Islands led me to buy some shares of the shipping company Nirvana, which happened after I encountered a truck on the autobahn that bore the slogan, «Nirvana—We deliver nothingness, from here to there.»

> The Cape Verdes Islands,
> a place where there is no advertising,
> no mobile phones —

Crazy.
The shares have lost half their value since yesterday. On top of

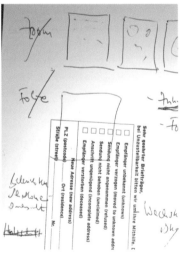

B H

I E

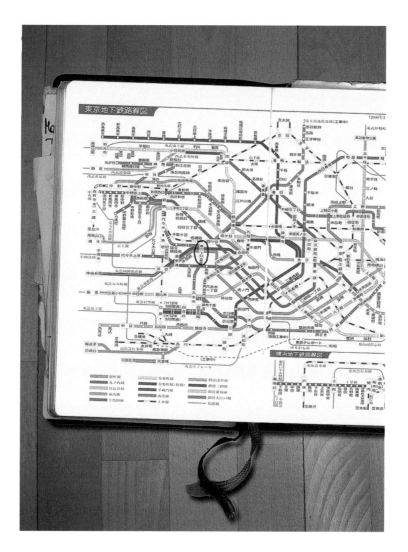

I

everything else. ~~Jubilant~~ prayer sisters proclaiming in two-part harmony while I was shaving, bearing the responsibility for un-ordered packages, a wet sock, a swollen toe. No ~~interest~~ now in the uninhibited Wittgenstein.

Or maybe Wittgenstein after all, but at home. Hand over the package. Wait until dark, when Brunnsteiner is irritating, one way or another. But was Brunnsteiner in his car yesterday? Were there birds to be heard? Was detergent missing? No matter.   What is the d e s c r i p t i o n of what I see?

(That does not just mean, what words should I use to describe what I see, but also, what does a description of what I see look like, what should I call it?)
String, brown packing paper, addressed with a blue ball-point. From: P.O. Box 8912 Gata/Boa Vista. To: B. Brunnsteiner.

Boa Vista?
It's certain that Brunnsteiner was not in his car yesterday.
I didn't hear any bird noises yesterday.

Boa Vista: that's an island and yesterday no detergent was miss-ing! If I hold the package firmly in my fingertips and turn it ~~slowly~~, something falls from here to there. First, have a drink. Bach Flower Remedies or bourbon or both.

B as in Brunnsteiner. What does that look like, a description of what I see?   I need to finish ~~shaving~~.

This package must not stay the n i g h t in my apartment.

The doorbell rings.

W

The Mystery of Lost Mystery

---   –

By Sandro Baldoni

---   –

I remember how shocked I was when, as a boy, I saw the big silver clad hoof of the first man to set foot on the Moon: I was overcome by a confused, instinctive mix of dejection, despair, betrayal. I let go of my father's hand—he was staring, open mouthed, at the television—, got out of the house and ran into the night, my heart beating hard, heading as fast as I could toward the place where I usually sat and looked at the moon, the derelict roof of an old, run down, bar-tobacconist.

When I reached the top of the stairs, the moon was hovering brightly in the sky, full, peaceful and resplendent as usual, as if nothing had changed.

The moon was pretending nothing had happened, but somehow I sensed, deep in my heart, that from that day on the Moon wouldn't be the same anymore. It was now officially on the list of substantial, concrete objects, numbered among the many commonplace things controlled by man, and had now ceased to be a mystery.

To my mind the moon landing was the beginning of the end of the great mysteries. With this act, our dangerous progeny had earnestly begun to take possession of the imponderable, in order to put it on the market.

This was perhaps the first step towards the creation of virtual reality, and all the trendy debates that have surrounded this pseudo-phenomenon.

The truth is, reality has never been so real. One just has to see the voracious speed at which every story is unearthed, analyzed, blown up on television for a worldwide audience and then just as quickly forgotten. Essentially, events are consumed by the market.

This leads to murderers owning up to their crimes live on television, in the hope of perhaps reaching pop star status, while the victims are on show right minutes after their death, with television cameras focusing on wounds and bruises, and the commentator interviewing the weeping relatives and providing a detailed account of their secrets, obsessions, and bank balance.

Everything, now has a somewhat pornographic dimension to it. In the sense that the speed with which reality is stripped of its dark areas, bared and presented to the public, leaves no time for asking questions, entertaining doubts, coming up with more or less plausible theories.

Reality transformed into show business kills all mystery, just as porn makes the mysteries of love trivial, debasing it to cheap consumer voyeurism.

We've just witnessed a pornographic war, with the dead, the wounded and the prisoners from all sides becoming cathode ray tube fodder well before being cannon fodder, obsessively filmed almost to the moment they draw their last breath. It's been the most »watched« war in history, with the strategies for the following day announced during the briefing sessions on the evening before, and the number of cameras zooming in on every movement of the troops outnumbering the enemy rifles.

But if you keep your eyes peeled, you'll notice that porn is working its way into all sorts of areas.

In books and in films, as is the case with love, foreplay no longer exists: stories go straight to the point, skipping character description, flying hysterically from one coup de théatre to the next, hell-bent on reaching a quick and mechanical ending, in the name of the standardisation of writing techniques, and afraid to tax the so-called audience's short attention span.

And what has happened to the aura of mystery surrounding show business stars, royalty and major political figures? Today we know Tom Cruise's favourite brand of underarm deodorant, because he advertises it himself, and everything there is to know about Madonna's sexual preference, because the lady herself broadcasts it in every direction on a daily basis, in the same way as we have had a blow by blow account of Lady Diana's love pinings and President Clinton's Oval office sexual exploits. Nor do religious mysteries escape unscathed either: Pope John Paul II had the bright idea of disclosing the Third Secret of Fatima on world television, modern-day Buddhists keep telling us that we are God and nothing else exists, and the staunch conservative Allah has now given us a Major Technological Spectacle courtesy of Osama Bin Laden, ridding us of the greatest (porno-phallic) symbol of all time in but the twinkling of an eye: and down went the Twin Towers.

Death is perhaps the only real unsolved mystery left.

But here again one cannot rest too easy: a pale and conceited American geneticist, Doctor Micheal Zey of Monclair State University, in an interview in the New York Times, claimed that as far as he was concerned by 2075 we may achieve the ultimate goal of immortality.

But he went on to explain that it won't come cheap, and he's on the look-out for sponsorship.

12 Collars

‒‒‒   ‒

By Jordan Crane

‒‒‒   ‒

I remember the first day
that I picked you up
and held you in my hands.
I wondered what you would end up like.
What would our relationship be like?
Would you protect me?
Make me laugh?
Be my friend?

For some of us the only thing that gets passed on between
generations are the dogs that our ancestors kept, hunted with,
and bred.

The Mighty Crusher, 1987–1994

Unknown, 1900's–1920's

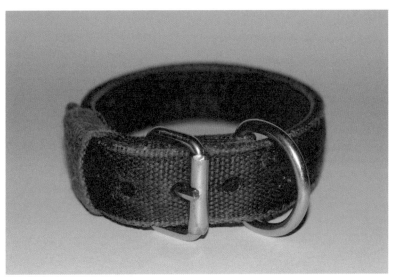

Bruno, 1993–present

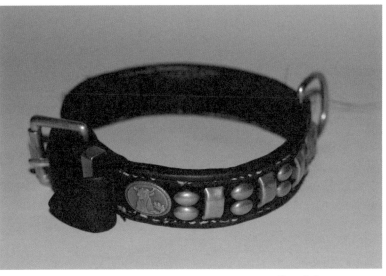

Crazy Lula, 1993–present

333 Wezen

Adell, 1995–2001

Cheeto, 1980–1993

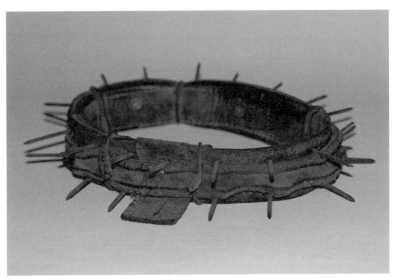

Unknown, 1870's–1900's

Miss Pinky, 1994–present

Big Reggie, 1990–2001

Lil' Miss Tina, 1985–1999

Lucky Stripe, 1993–present

Unknown, 1920's–1930's

Wolpertinger

By freude with Wolfgang Zajc

Don't ever get them wet.

Keep them away from water.

important thing,

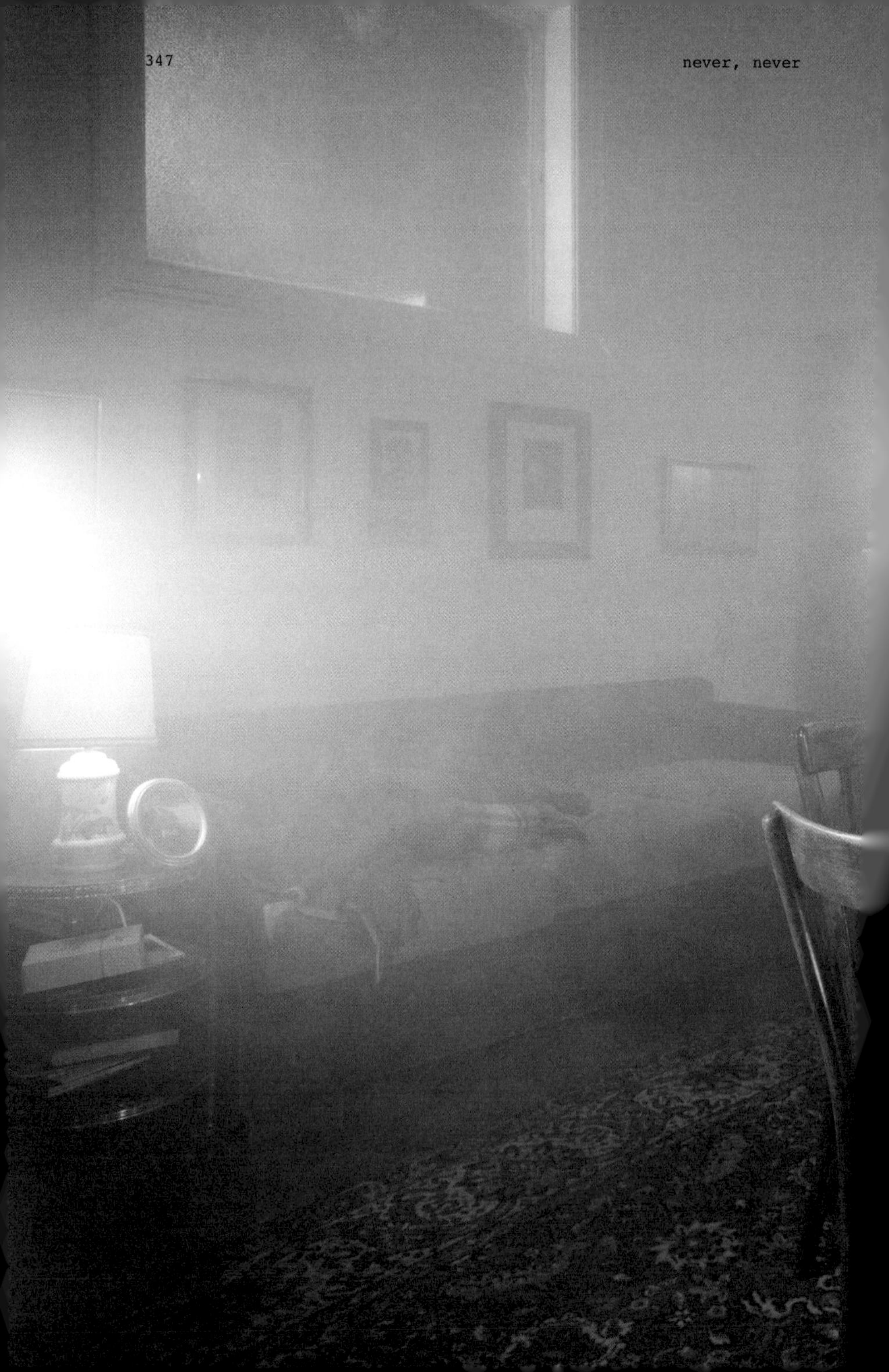

Have You Seen?

By Anke Dessin

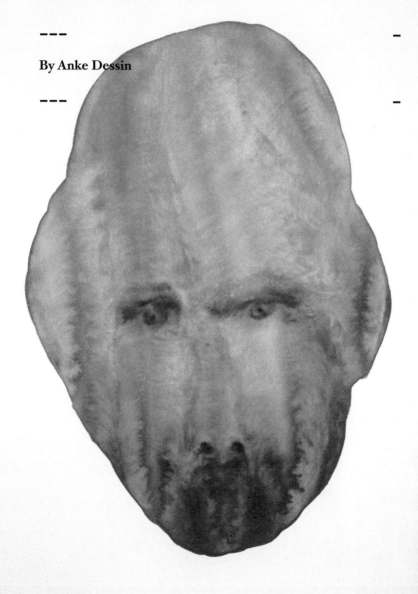

It's what's in their heart.

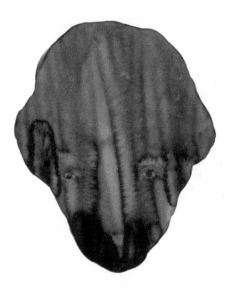

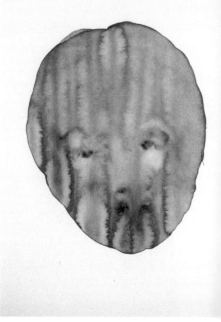

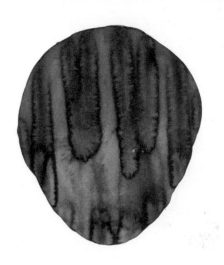

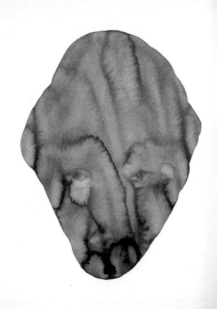

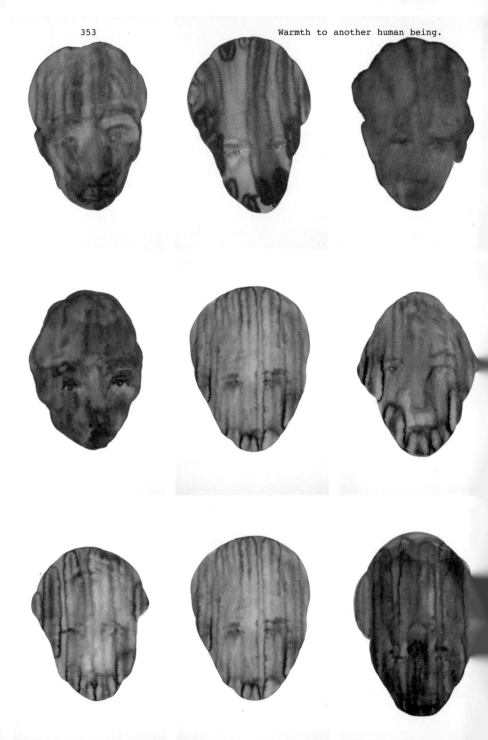

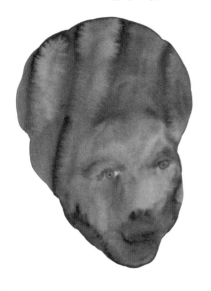
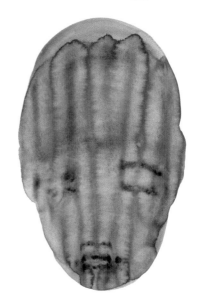

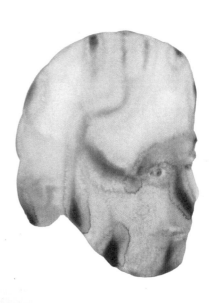

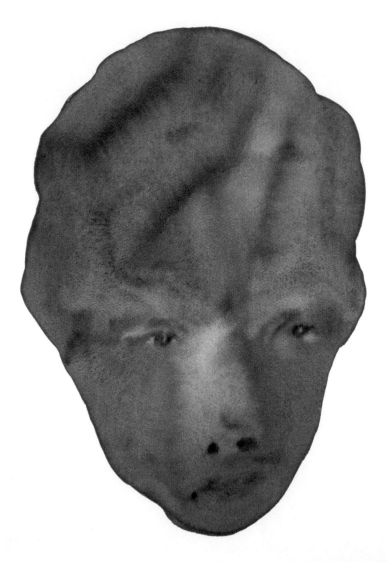

Who knows of someone who looks alike one of these characters, please send your observations in writing with or without a picture to: headdessin@web.de

Voices from the Beyond

---   -

By Andreas Schett

---   -

Rosemary Brown was a widow and housewife living in a London suburb. In 1964 the greatest composers in music history started paying visits to her at her home. Bach, Schubert, Liszt (and however else they're called, the masters of composition) dictated brand-new pieces of music to her, pieces they had composed after their demise. When Rosemary died four years ago she left more than 400 compositions, two records and the book «Unfinished Symphonies. Voices from the Beyond,» through which Andreas Schett has leafed more than once.

```
«Sender: +4369910137788 Sent: 09:42:34 26.02.2004
The medium is speaking —»
«Sender: +4369919436917 Sent: 09:43:56 26.02.2004
My heart is trembling with joy.»
```

Let's start with the blurb:

«There are mountains, rivers, forests and lots of beautiful flowers on the other side, and the people there look a lot younger, handsomer and healthier. They study languages, paint pictures, compose...»
This piece of information as well as numerous others were provided

by Liszt, Schubert, Beethoven and Bach, all in all by twelve very famous musicians, who dictated their latest works, composed on the other side, to Rosemary Brown.
The medium took down more than 400 pieces of music, some in front of television cameras, in no time. Scientists, eminent composers and psychologists have stated: Rosemary Brown's music from the beyond is, amazing though it may seem, genuine.

«I'm just the receiver.»

«I receive things as they come.»

«There can be no doubt about Mrs. Brown's gift as a medium.»
(Der Spiegel)

And now, right away, a good story:

In 1969 some people of BBC Three asked me whether I was willing to co-operate in producing a documentary on my work. Frankly, I had my doubts. When I got this offer I asked Liszt what he thought about it. He had no doubts at all. «You simply must do it,» he said. Part of the programme consisted of a meticulous interrogation, an experience we're all familiar with. Then they asked me something I have been asked many times before: was I willing or able to get in touch with a composer live on the programme? «I'll try» I said, «but I can't guarantee anything.» The BBC people accepted this. We gathered in the room where I work. I brought in some tea and waited for things to happen. After only a few minutes Liszt appeared, dependable as usual. He looked very calm and composed and said he was going to try to communicate a new piece to me. «Make it something really special, if possible,» I said to him, and he smiled knowingly. First he gave me the clef. «It is six sharps,» he said, «the time is 5/4 for the right hand and 3/2 for the left.» This was very difficult. I turned around, annoyed, and saw that he was smiling complacently. He had never communicated music this difficult to me before. «Just try,» Liszt said soothingly, «go on.» The score was much too difficult for me to play at sight. I simply couldn't manage to play 5/4 and 3/2 time together and I got more and more confused. Then the editor asked me whether I'd mind if he had a go. I had not been aware until then that he was a good pianist. It sounded very interesting, and when he had finished the room was completely silent. He then turned around very slowly and said: «Mrs. Brown, I believe there really is something in it.» That took a weight off my mind!

Liszt, indeed. He first visited Rosemary Brown when she was still a child. Rosy had just woken up when she saw a man in a black cassock and with long white hair standing beside her bed. «When you have grown up I will come back and give you music,» he said.

That took some time: Rosemary Brown's husband had already died of hepatic cirrhosis, she had to earn a living for herself and her two children aged eight and four and a half and accepted a job as a kitchen help; early 1960s, London, great hardship. Then Liszt came. «Probably (he) had to wait for the right time.» Initially the quiet presence of the white-haired man was simply «a great comfort;» no mention of music. One day, when Rosemary was wondering where to get money from to buy presents for her children, Liszt advised her: Perhaps you should try the football pools. She won, first 10 Pounds and the 51 Pounds. Can Mrs. Brown foretell the correct results? (So convenient!) — «The answer is simple: I can't do it and I never shall.»

In any event, it happened right during this time: the awakening —

I had an accident. I believe I had two ribs broken, but no x-ray was made at the hospital and so I'll probably never know. I was on sick leave for a week and was told to do as little as possible. I spent my time reading and doing some knitting, and one day it occurred to me to go and play the piano for a while. That afternoon Liszt visited me. I saw him standing beside me clearly and distinctly. And instead of selecting a piece of music and playing it I suddenly felt that he

*was guiding my hands on the piano. The music sounded without my
doing, and it was music I had never heard before. Today Liszt is the
organizer and leader of a group of celebrated composers who visit
me at my home and give their latest compositions to me.*

So many notes, and that's not all: Liszt extinguishes fires that
have broken out in the house and points out special offers to
Rosemary while she is doing her shopping, and:

*Strange as it may seem: I think I can rightly say that Liszt has become
a good friend to me. We chat about all kinds of things, serious things,
like the meaning of life and metaphysical issues.*

*He is so very handsome and he has beautiful manners. He is grace-
ful and dignified. And he is romantic in himself. He says such charm-
ing things and one can't help thinking: «Well, here's someone who
knows the art of chivalry.»*

*Let me give you another example to demonstrate how deeply Liszt
has got involved in the life of my family: how one day he helped my
son Thomas doing his homework. One evening Thomas was doing
his algebra homework and asked me: «Mummy, how much is one to
the power of two plus two to the power of two plus three to the
power of two plus four to the power of two plus...» Even before he
had finished the sentence Liszt, who was with me, said: «Three-
hundred and eighty-five.»*

Moreover, Liszt has meanwhile learned to speak perfect
English — an achievement, after all, that Bach can hardly lay a
claim to.

*Bach is a strict man. Actually I don't really enjoy working with
him. He seems to have no sense of humour. I have never seen him
smile yet and he always behaves in a very reserved manner, but perhaps that's only when he is with me. When he comes to my house it's
only work, work and yet more work. I admire and respect him tre-*

mendously, but I have never succeeded in getting really close to him. He speaks a little English, which I suppose he has taught himself over there, because I don't think he could speak English when he was still alive. I would like to ask him, but I just don't dare to do that! I am here only to receive his music, and that's it.

Just a minute: that's not fair. Why HER of all people?

The answer to the question, «Why you of all people?» is somewhat more complex, but Liszt explained that to me. I asked him the same question—«Why me?»—and he said: «Because you were ready for it, indeed ready for it a long time before you were born.»

There you are. It certainly wasn't a question of musical ability. They accuse me of having had a sound musical education, Rosemary complains, but fiddlesticks. One year of practising on a piano out of tune in an unheated parlour in her parents' house when she was little; during her girlhood lessons with a graduate of the Royal Academy for two semesters, for which she paid herself; then the war; finally, once more, 1951-52, shortly before she got married: piano lessons.

So, if they chose me as the medium and appointed this task for me, I asked Liszt, why then wasn't I born into a family where I could have got a better musical education? «Your education is sufficient for our purposes,» he said. «If you had had a really comprehensive education this would be of no use at all to us. First of all a comprehensive musical education would have made it even more difficult for you to prove that you couldn't have composed our music on your own. Secondly, a profound understanding of music might have caused you to develop your own ideas and theories, and these would have been inconvenient for us.»

Like we said, Rosemary didn't have the foggiest—

*I often think that one should really take the time and listen careful-
ly, but unless the piece of music is very short and interesting it soon
starts to bore me and I get nervous. Unfortunately I am much too
active a person to sit still and listen. In any case I'm not able at all
to say which music was written by whom. Sometimes I turn on the
radio and say to my daughter, «That's Schubert! No, it's Mozart. Or
perhaps Beethoven?» I get it wrong almost every time.*

Enter Schubert:

*I find Schubert an amiable person. I think everybody would like
him.*

*If I remember correctly he was wearing glasses the first time. I
think he did that only to make it easier for me to recognize him;
after all, on the other side he doesn't need glasses and he has never
worn them since when visiting me. I noticed that Schubert was a
truly handsome man, particularly since he doesn't look so fat and
chubby-cheeked as he is usually depicted. He's extremely modest and
inconspicuous, in his own way very quiet and cheerful, only his
humour is somewhat old-fashioned.*

*By the way, when we're working on his songs he sometimes attempts
to sing them to me. Unfortunately, his voice isn't very good. I had
imagined that on your arrival on the other side you immediately get
a good singing voice, but this conflicts with my assumption.*

*I have even heard the end of the Unfinished Symphony, which is
really exceptionally beautiful. Schubert let me hear it through tele-
pathy. Some of the composers can do that and they are also able to
«compress» time in a way that enables me to actually hear an entire
concerto or a symphony within only a few minutes. I hope that one
day I will be able to take down the last movement of Schubert's
Unfinished Symphony for him—but I suppose that will be a lengthy
and difficult task.*

When Schubert gives me a piece of music he usually asks anxiously afterwards, «Did you like it?,» as though he was a little insecure and needed to be reassured. In any case he is not really sure of his ground there.

Schubert doesn't wear glasses anymore, and, incidentally, Beethoven is no longer deaf!

For a long time Beethoven remained a mystery to me. Of course he's not deaf anymore. These human afflictions and ailments disappear on the other side. Sometimes he talks about music, sometimes about himself, about life or God. One day he spoke to me so softly and kindly that I said to him, deeply moved and humbly: «Beethoven— I love you!» He just looked at me with the suspicion of a smile and said quite seriously: «Of course.»

It was the same Beethoven who lost his nerve. «Beethoven left no doubt that he would consider the communication of his music a waste of time if no effort was made to make it known.» Thus at some point the BBC entered the scene. How that came about?

Mrs. Brown's mother was lying on her deathbed. «Promise me one thing,» she said to her daughter, «when I'm dead go and see Mrs. Hosgood, promise me that you'll go and see her.» Rosemary promised it, and only a few days after her mother's funeral she found Mrs. Hosgood, a clairvoyant married to a rescue service official, actually standing right in front of her door. «Your mother sends me!,» she said. Rosemary attended the séances at Mrs. Hosgood's, where she then met one Mrs. Pendleton, who played the organ during services at the spiritualist church and was looking for somebody to stand in for her when she was unable to attend. Rosemary couldn't refuse but made «the most terrible mistakes while the congregation were singing». So she often used to sneak into the church to practice secretly. At some point she decided to give it up. «I ask you urgently to continue,» said Liszt. «It is of utmost importance!»

Practizing again. One Saturday afternoon: one Mrs. Glady Smith is offering occult counseling at the same time, and only one client comes to see her as the famous healer Mr. Edwards is in town that day. Mrs. Glady Smith has no choice but to wait and see whether any other people will show up. While she is waiting she hears Rosemary play the organ (Liszt has already started to communicate music).

«Play on!» And: «Who wrote this?»
«The music has been spiritually inspired, so to speak.»
«You have no idea who inspired it? Was it any particular person?»
«I believe it could be Liszt.»

Mrs. Smith knows some people in Wimbledon, an association for occult and spiritualist research, including Hilary Wontner and his wife Judith, who in turn are acquainted in some way with Betty Francis and her husband Karl, and that is how a contact to Mary Rogers is established and an encounter with Sir George Trevelyan takes place one day, who in his turn shows the scores scribbled down by Rosemary to one Mrs. Mary Firth, who is joined by a certain Major MacManaway, whereupon the three last mentioned persons set up a foundation so as to enable Rosemary to spend more time on the music, when one day Monica Sims of the BBC is on the phone, which terribly upsets Sir George and Mrs. Firth... well, Rosemary does it anyway. In the interest of the composers from the beyond—

But now back to work:

I believe there are others still waiting, «behind the scenes,» so to speak, to join the group and communicate their music. They are all welcome to me, of course. My only problem is how to find enough time to do all the work they're planning for me.

We have developed a method of work that I try to adhere to. I send the children to school, do the housework, and then work on the

music from about 10 a.m. until 1 p.m. The composer working with me on that day then leaves me so that I can have lunch and reappears at around half past one. We then continue to work until about half past four. At that time I have to stop working to prepare dinner for the children. In the evenings, though, we get back to work again, and on the weekends, too.

With all these duties to see to on one single day a guy like Debussy is nothing but trouble:

Debussy is not one of my regular visitors. He is at times somewhat fickle. Sometimes he appears every day, and then again I don't see him at all for a long time. I had already received a number of piano pieces from him and he had started working on a septet but had not got very far with it. I think it will turn out a very interesting piece, but my son Thomas doesn't like it. Whenever I play the themes on the piano he hides away because the music seems so very disharmonious to him.

I believe that Debussy was in a sense a victim of the conventions of his time. Nowadays thousands of people live like he used to; they wear strange clothes and sometimes sleep with women who are not their wives. Today nobody cares much about these things, but in his day that was different.

The most interesting aspect about Debussy is perhaps that he has started painting on the other side. He has also painted two pictures which he named «Sunrise» and «Sunset.» Naturally, their colours are those of the sunlight, with red and orange prevailing. The pictures are lovely and it really is a pity that the world cannot see them. I find Debussy highly amusing. He is usually depicted wearing a beard but now he is clean-shaven.

And the best news comes last—it's true:

I have already pointed out earlier the different theories people come up with in order to explain away my music. One of them says that I «suffer» from cryptomnesia, hidden memory. Another one suggests that something may be wrong with my state of mind. Well, they're both wrong, and I am gratified to state that one of the world's leading experts in the field of parapsychology has performed extensive tests with me and that the results of the tests disprove both these theories. The parapsychologist is Professor Tenhaeff. When Philips released the first LP of the composers' music I was asked whether I would be willing to undergo extensive tests to be performed by Professor Tenhaeff and his team. In a communication to the worldwide press he stated: «The results show that we are dealing with a mentally healthy woman who is not keen on being the centre of attention. Rather the opposite is true. My assistant, a resident psychiatrist with many years of professional experience, did not note any mental abnormality. Our psychodiagnostic examination did not show the slightest indication of a mental malformation, either. Further tests are planned, in which renowned music experts will also take part. Of the numerous cases I have learned of over many years that of Rosemary Brown is definitely one of the most interesting. Besides, she is one of the most likeable and moreover one of the most reasonable people.» In spite of the many difficulties that I am faced with I am very happy that the music from the beyond is finally appreciated. And I hope that some day the world will recognize this music as a true gift from the other side and that the efforts of the composers will thus not have been in vain.

Let us give as much credit to Rosemary Brown's words as to those of Nikolaus Harnoncourt—

My Mysteryland

---   -

By Mike Meiré

---   -

But what if you are trying

So on Saturday,

we cracked open a new roll,

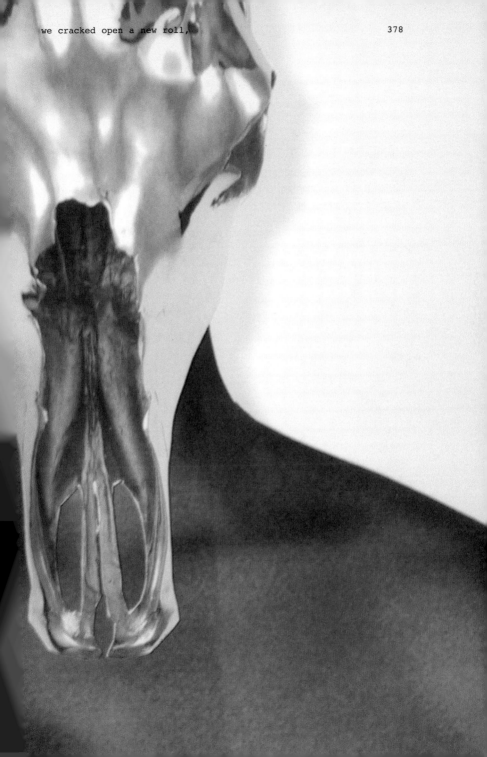

Eve: «I'll take care of the rest of this fruit.»

Naturally Tasty

---   –

A Dialogue[1] Between Silke Stock and Daniel Roth

«A piece of information becomes a message, becomes an action. Of course *Naturally Tasty* does not hesitate to perform this action. I capture the actions in my drawings and collages and maybe I pass them on.»[2]

3a)

3b)

Rekonstruktion des Flugsauriers Ornithocheirus
Mesozoikums-Saal

DAS NATUR
HISTORISCHE
MUSEUM
WIEN

Wenn Du mal nach Wien kommst
mußt Du unbedingt ins
Naturhistorische Museum.
Das wird Dich begeistern, bestimmt.

© Naturhistorisches Museum Wien, 1040/2000

completely missed the point of the Tree.»

completely missed the point of the Tree.»

completely missed the point of the Tree.» 384

4)

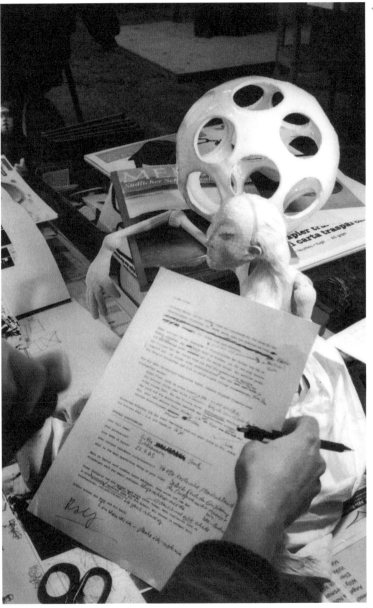

5a-c)

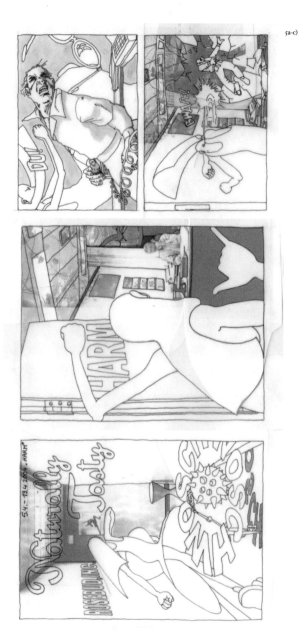

5d-e)

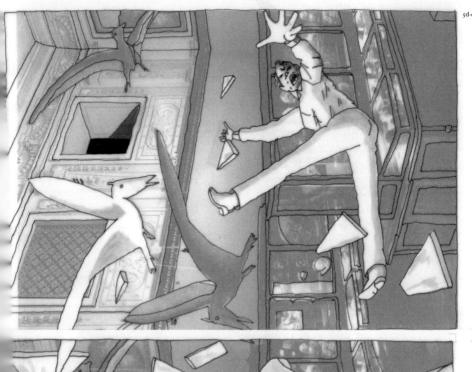

Eve: «Yeah, can't disobey without a Tree.»

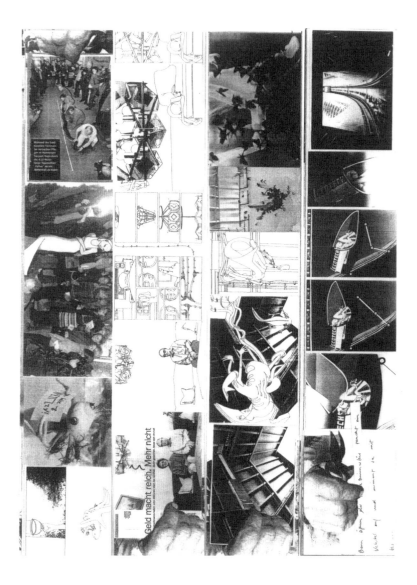

NOTES:

p. 381, 387, 388 and 390: Rough scans of contributed material which mysteriously disappeared during the editing process. See also footnote 4).

1) Dialogue: i) A conversation between two or more people. ii) Conversation between characters in a drama or narrative. iii) The lines or passages in a script that are intended to be spoken. iv) A literary work written in the form of a conversation: the dialogues of Plato. v) Music. A composition or passage for two or more parts, suggestive of conversational interplay. vi) An exchange of ideas or opinions: achieving constructive dialogue with all political elements. *(The American Heritage Dictionary of the English Language)*

2) Artist Silke Stock on her working principle.

3a-b) Postcard from Daniel Roth to Silke Stock: «Whenever you happen to come to Vienna, make sure to visit the Natural History Museum. You will love it. Definitely.»

4) Silke Stock and *Naturally Tasty* reading a letter from the editor. [A principle of communication in general holds that, for communication to take place, at least two parties are needed. If one party disappears, communication stops. In this specific case disappearance* itself caused communication.]

   * «I can't really say a lot about its disappearance. I guess it is a mystery. Maybe you should take
     another look. Maybe they slipped under the couch. Supposing they really vanished into thin air,
     there is not a lot we can do about it. Things like that happen.»

5) **harm I** *s*. **1**. Schaden *m*: **bodily _** körperlicher Schaden, Körperverletzung *f*; **come to -** zu Schaden kommen; **do _ to s.o.** j-m schaden, j-m et. antun; **(there is) no _ done!** es ist nichts (Schlimmes) passiert!; **it does more _ than good** es schadet mehr, als dass es nützt; **there is no _ in doing (s.th.)** es kann od. könnte nicht schaden, (et.) zu tun; **mean no _** es nicht böse meinen; **keep out of _'s way** a) in Sicherheit, b) in sicherer Entfernung; **2.** Unrecht *n*, Übel *n*; **II** *v/t.* **3.** schaden (*dat.*), *j-n* verletzen (*a. fig.*); **harm·ful** *adj.* nachteilig, schädlich (**to** für): **_ publications** jugendgefährdende Schriften; **harm·ful·ness** *s.* Schädlichkeit *f*; **harm·less** *adj.* **1.** harmlos: a) unschädlich, ungefährlich, b) unschuldig, arglos, c) unverfänglich; **2. keep** (*od.* **save**) **s.o. _** j-n schadlos halten; **harm·lessness** *s.* Harmlosigkeit *f*. *(Langenscheidts Handwörterbuch Englisch-Deutsch)*

6) «Naturally Tasty» – Fruits and vegetables tag

Wahrscheinlichkeit, dass ein Patient in Deutschland sein Rezept für
Arzneimittel nicht einlöst oder – wenn er es einlöst – die verschriebenen
Medikamente nicht oder falsch anwendet, in Prozent: 60

Weitaus mehr als nur Zahlen.

Adam: (dropping his axe) «Well you're no fun!»

6)

Deutsche Texte

Seite 26

Von Katzen, Quanten und Cephalopoden

___   –

von Peter Schattschneider

___   –

Vorbemerkung

Dieser Essay wurde 1992 geschrieben. Viel hat sich inzwischen getan, und auch
wieder nicht. Die eigentümlichen Gesetze der Quantenmechanik wurden aufs
Glänzendste bestätigt. Wir können jetzt einzelne Atome in einer unwirklichen
Überlagerung von weder-hier-noch-dort beobachten, so genannten «cat states»,
Lichtteilchen werden unter scheinbarer Nichtbeachtung der Relativitätstheo-
rie teleportiert und Riesenmoleküle bringen es fertig, jedes für sich gleichzeitig
durch zwei weit voneinander entfernte Löcher zu fliegen.[1] Die Rolle des Be-
obachters ist insofern relativiert worden, als der Übergang zur klassischen
Betrachtungsweise eher mit dem Verschwinden von Interferenztermen inner-
halb sehr kurzer Zeiten zu tun hat als mit dem Beobachten. Trotzdem bleibt die
Quantenmechanik rätselhaft. Man ist heute, im neuen Jahrtausend und hundert
Jahre nach ihrer Einführung, mindestens so weit von einem Verständnis ihrer
Gesetze entfernt wie damals. Es war daher zum Erstaunen und zur Freude des
Autors gar nicht nötig, den Text groß umzuschreiben. Die wesentlichste Ände-
rung betrifft die Umstellung der österreichischen Währung auf den Euro.

«Ist es nicht verwunderlich, dass Katzen genau dort die Löcher im Fell
haben, wo die Augen sitzen?», fragte Georg Christoph Lichtenberg, jener Physiker aus dem 18. Jahrhundert, der uns Physik und Aphorismen hinterlassen hat.

Die Physiker mögen Katzen und Verwunderliches. Es gebe welche, die
weder tot noch lebendig seien, behauptete zwei Jahrhunderte später Erwin
Schrödinger, der eine Zeit lang die österreichischen Tausend-Schilling-Noten
geziert hat. (Mozart war um ATS 5000,– zu haben, was die relative Bedeutung
von Wissenschaft und Kunst in jenem verwunderlichen Land recht genau
wiedergibt).

Nach dieser Einstimmung lassen wir Schrödingers Katze aus dem Sack
und zum Vorschein werden noch ihr Großvater und ihre Kinder kommen.
Zuerst aber wollen wir das Biotop beschreiben, in dem diese eigenwillige Krea-
tur ihr Unwesen treibt.

Quanten – eine hoffnungslose Schweinerei

Max Planck stieß gegen 1900 im Zuge von Forschungen für die boomende Berliner Glühlampenindustrie auf eine neue Naturkonstante, die bewirkt, dass Strahlungsenergie nicht kontinuierlich, sondern in Paketen – quantisiert – abgegeben wird. Es lohnt, an dieser Stelle sich darüber klar zu werden, dass quantisierte Energie in einer bis dahin stetigen, homogenen, glatten Physik absolut unpassend war – wie eine Rap-Einlage in der Finlandia oder wie Kubismus bei Rubens. Max Planck mochte seine Hilfsgröße h, wie er sie nannte, gar nicht. Eine allgemeine Verstörung unter den Physikern hub an und sie sollte an die dreißig Jahre anhalten.

1927 erst konnte Werner Heisenberg eine stimmige «Quantenmechanik» präsentieren, wie die Theorie vom Mikrokosmos bald genannt wurde. Dass die Formulierung einer Theorie 27 Jahre dauerte, lag nicht etwa an der Faulheit jener ersten Riege von Physikern, sondern daran, dass die Quantenmechanik scheinbar vielen bisher als vernünftig betrachteten Begriffen widersprach – oder wie Max Born, einer ihrer Proponenten, es ausdrückte: «Die Quanten sind doch eine hoffnungslose Schweinerei.»

Wie tief die mit der neuen Theorie hereingebrochenen erkenntnistheoretischen Probleme waren, wird schon im einleitenden Satz von Heisenbergs Originalarbeit deutlich: «In der vorliegenden Arbeit werden zunächst exakte Definitionen der Worte: Ort, Geschwindigkeit, Energie usw. aufgestellt [...].»[2]

Es nimmt nicht wunder, dass angesichts solcher Zweifel an den Grundlagen der exaktesten aller Wissenschaften die Scientific Community zutiefst beunruhigt war.

In der postmodernen Physik würde man das Problem wahrscheinlich anders angehen, die Worte Ort, Geschwindigkeit, Energie sein lassen und statt dessen eine probabilistische Fernwirkung postulieren; aber heute werden Theorien anders entworfen, information is the message, Hauptsache, wir veröffentlichen früher als andere.[3] Freilich würde auch eine postmoderne Quantenmechanik das Grundproblem nicht umgehen können, das die Physiker um Niels Bohr glaubten, mit der «Kopenhagener Deutung» der Theorie beseitigt zu haben, die bis heute die offizielle philosophische Grundlage für den eigentümlichen Formalismus der Quantenmechanik ist. Aber die Dinge neigen nun mal dazu, sich nicht an offizielle Lesarten zu halten. Verordnungen können das kollektive Glück, die Wahrheit oder die Wirklichkeit genau so wenig bestimmen wie Sicherheitsvorschriften Katastrophen in Atomkraftwerken verhindern. Tatsächlich hatte die Kopenhagener Schule das Grundproblem der Quantenmechanik nur so gut versteckt, dass es ein halbes Jahrhundert unauffindbar blieb. Diese sorgfältige Tarnung verführte namhafte Naturwissenschaftler zu abenteuerlichen Thesen über die Rolle des menschlichen

Bewusstseins bei der Messung von Ort, Geschwindigkeit, Energie, etc., sogar
außersinnliche Wahrnehmung wurde vom Physiker Eugene Wigner bemüht.[4]

Auch Schrödingers Katze ist ein Produkt dieses Grundproblems, das entgegen
allen anders lautenden Behauptungen durchaus ohne physikalische Kenntnisse
verstanden werden kann; sehr wahrscheinlich beruht diese Meinung auf der
Tatsache, dass eine fehlende Physikausbildung das Verständnis des Problems
durchaus erleichtert. Wir werden es an einem einfachen Beispiel erläutern, das
als Vorläufer von Schrödingers Katze gelten kann, und dieses Beispiel heranzie-
hen, um die wunderliche Geschichte des Tieres bis ins Jahr 1982 zu verfolgen.

Der Katzengroßvater

Licht ist bekanntlich eine Wellenbewegung. Von einer Lichtquelle gehen wie
von einem in ruhiges Wasser geworfenen Stein Wellenfronten aus. Diese Wellen
können reflektiert, gebrochen, überlagert werden – alles gehorcht den Gesetzen der Wellenlehre, die aus manchen schönen Schulversuchen mit der
«Wellenwanne» bekannt sind. Indem wir nun statt Licht Wasserwelle sagen und
statt Lichtquelle geworfener Stein, haben wir ein Modell der Lichtausbreitung,
an dem wir alle in diesem Zusammenhang interessierenden Phänomene, insbesondere das angesprochene Grundproblem der Quantenmechanik, studieren
können.

Was wir noch nicht haben, ist ein Analogon zur Beobachtung der
Erscheinungen. Lichtwellen sind ja nicht sichtbar wie Wasserwellen. Wenn der
Physiker optische Phänomene untersuchen will, bringt er einen Film (es kann
auch die lichtempfindliche Netzhaut seines Auges sein) in den Lichtweg ein. In
unserem Modell ersetzen wir den Film durch einen Sandstrand, auf den die
Wasserwellen auftreffen. So wie der Film geschwärzt wird, hinterlassen die
Wasserwellen Vertiefungen im Sand. Bei genauer Betrachtung des entwickelten
Films unter der Lupe stellt sich nun heraus, dass die Emulsion aus einzelnen
Bromsilberkörnern besteht. Drosseln wir die Intensität der Lichtquelle, dann
werden nicht etwa die einzelnen Körner kleiner, sondern weniger Körner wer-
den geschwärzt, wie jeder Amateurfotograf weiß. Bei genügend kurzer Be-
lichtungszeit sehen wir bloß ein einziges Korn auf dem Film – der vorgebildete
Leser weiß, dass diese Schwärzung von dem einem Photon herrührt, das von der
Lichtquelle ausgesendet wurde.

Wir brauchen also noch ein Analogon für Photonen (Dinge, welche ein
Korn schwärzen können) in unserem Modell: Denken wir uns dafür kleine
Boote oder vielleicht Nussschalen. Man ist nun geneigt anzunehmen, dass von
dem geworfenen Stein Nussschalen losgerissen werden, mit den Wellen weg-

treiben und dort, wo sie das Ufer erreichen, Vertiefungen im Sand hinterlassen.
Es ist wichtig zu erkennen, dass die Wellen nichts mit der Schwärzung zu tun
haben können, da sie keine punktförmigen Vertiefungen (einzelne belichtete
Bromsilbermoleküle), sondern ausgedehnte Dünen erzeugen würden – was niemals beobachtet wird. Man stellte bald fest, dass die Nussschalen merkwürdige Eigenschaften
haben müssen. Wir können zum Beispiel vor dem Ufer eine Hafenmauer mit
zwei Einfahrten bauen und die Nussschalen werden nun keineswegs mehr gleich-
mäßig verteilt, sondern im selben charakteristischen Streifenmuster angeschwemmt, das die einander überlagernden Wellen zeigen (Die Physiker sagen
dazu Interferenz). Schließt man eine der beiden Öffnungen, dann bleiben nicht
etwa einige Nussschalen aus, sondern die durch die andere Einfahrt kommen-
den ändern plötzlich ihren Kurs, als wüssten sie, dass die zweite, weit entfernte
Einfahrt soeben gesperrt wurde. Die Häufungen der Nussschalen (die man
natürlich erst nach einiger Zeit bemerkt, wenn genügend viele angeschwemmt
wurden) finden sich immer dort, wo die Wellen hoch sind.

Es gibt nun zwei Deutungsmöglichkeiten für diese Geschichte: Entweder nimmt
man an, dass die Nussschalen intelligent sind und wissen, was weit entfernt von
ihnen in diesem Augenblick geschieht (sie müssten also sogar außersinnlicher
Wahrnehmung fähig sein) – dann kann man aber auf die Wellen ganz verzichten;
oder man behält das Wellenkonzept bei, das die Verteilung der Nussschalen so
schön und richtig beschreibt – dann kann man aber auf die Nussschalen verzichten. In der Tat werden sie ja erst am Strand beobachtet, niemals vorher![9]
Wir stehen also vor der Entscheidung, intelligente Nussschalen mit außersinnlicher Wahrnehmung zu akzeptieren oder anzunehmen, dass sie erst am
Ufer entstehen, und zwar umso häufiger, je höher die Wellen sind. Wir haben
hier das Grundproblem der Quantenmechanik freipräpariert, jenen Punkt, der
unseren Erfahrungen eklatant widerspricht. Unser Verständnis sträubt sich
sowohl gegen Nussschalen mit außersinnlicher Wahrnehmung als auch gegen
die Autogenese von Gegenständen bei hohem Wellengang – genauer: Aus hohem Wellengang, denn das Merkwürdigste am Verhalten der Wellen ist, dass der
gesamte Wellenzug mit Erscheinen einer Nussschale überall zusammenbricht
– als wäre der Teich im Handumdrehen spiegelglatt (auf das Experiment mit
Lichtwellen übertragen: sobald das Photon im Film absorbiert ist, wird es finster).

Die Physiker um Niels Bohr waren der Meinung, dass die zweite Annahme das
kleinere Übel sei. Darin waren sich Bohr und Einstein ausnahmsweise einig, wie
folgender Ausspruch Einsteins zeigt: «Der Gedanke, dass [...] ein Elektron aus
freiem Entschluss den Augenblick und die Richtung wählt, in der es fortsprin-
gen will, ist mir unerträglich. Wenn schon, dann möchte ich lieber Schuster oder

gar Angestellter in einer Spielbank sein als Physiker.» Seien wir froh, dass
Einstein die noch zu schildernde Entwicklung nicht voraussah; er hätte sehr
wahrscheinlich seinen Beruf gewechselt.

Aber auch das kleinere Übel, das zur heute anerkannten Deutung führte,
erzeugte Unbehagen. Die Kopenhagener Gruppe um Bohr versteckte es hinter
einem eleganten Formalismus, der die Beobachtungen exakt beschrieb. Der
geniale Schritt bestand darin, jene sich ausbreitenden Wellen, die bei Erscheinen einer Nussschale wie durch Geisterhand zusammenbrechen, als Wahrscheinlichkeit zu deuten (die Höhe der Welle an einem bestimmten Punkt gibt
die Wahrscheinlichkeit an, dass dort eine Nussschale entsteht). Die Welle mit
der seltsamen Eigenschaft, Nussschalen zu erzeugen und dann weiß der Teufel
wie zusammenzubrechen, war also nichts Reales, sondern man durfte sie sich als
«potentia» oder «propensity», wie Karl Popper später sagte, als bloße Möglich-
keit, dass dort etwas geschieht, vorstellen – gewissermaßen ein erkenntnistheo-
retischer Schwindel, der die Idee einer auf geheimen Befehl plötzlich und überall zusammenbrechenden Welle erträglicher machen sollte. Diese Deutung
klärte vorläufig, was Erwin Schrödinger eigentlich gefunden hatte, als er 1926
seine berühmte Wellengleichung entdeckte. Sie funktionierte zwar, aber niemand wusste, was sie beschrieb. Die Lage wurde von den Physikern als hoff-
nungslos, aber nicht ernst eingeschätzt, wie folgendes lyrisches Statement eines
Kollegen Schrödingers zeigt:

Gar manches rechnet Erwin schon
mit seiner Wellenfunktion.
Nur wissen möcht' man gerne wohl,
was man sich dabei vorstell'n soll.[6]

In der «Kopenhagener Deutung» des quantenmechanischen Formalismus
ist die Wahrscheinlichkeit die eigentliche physikalische Größe, sie ist durch
eine Zahl zwischen Null und Eins gegeben, die einer relativ einfachen Gleichung, der Schrödinger-Gleichung, gehorcht und daher exakt vorausberechnet
werden kann. Das Konzept einer Wahrscheinlichkeitswelle ist zwar abstrakt,
aber vertraut, da sie sich so verhält, wie man es von Wellen gewohnt ist. Man
beachte, dass der Zufall hier einem Gesetz (in Form der Schrödinger-
Gleichung) gehorcht. Entschließt man sich aber zu einer Messung (die Welle auf
den Strand treffen zu lassen), dann stört, ja zerstört man diese Gesetzmäßigkeit:
Die Nussschale materialisert irgendwo, den Gesetzen der Wahrscheinlichkeit
gehorchend, die Welle bricht zusammen und vergisst die Gleichung. Die Beobachtung setzt die Gleichung außer Kraft. Es sieht ganz so aus, als wäre das
Verhalten von Wellen und Nussschalen davon abhängig, ob wir messen oder
nicht. Das ist der oft zitierte Einfluss des Beobachters auf das Messobjekt und

man erkennt jetzt, dass dieser vermeintliche Einfluss durch die oben getroffene Wahl des kleineren Übels entstanden ist. Hätten wir uns für Nussschalen mit außersinnlicher Wahrnehmung entschieden, gäbe es keinen «Einfluss des Beobachters», da es keine Wellen gäbe, die zusammenbrechen, wenn der Beobachter hinsieht.

So problematisch die erkenntnistheoretische Begründung der Quantenmechanik war – sie funktionierte! Die neuen Formeln beschrieben die atomaren Energieniveaus, die Elektronenbeugung, die Radioaktivität und vieles andere mit fantastischer Genauigkeit – und dabei ist es bis heute geblieben. Roger Penrose formulierte das so: «Die Theorie hat zwei sehr wirksame Argumente für sich und nur ein kleines gegen sich. Erstens, die Theorie stimmt in unglaublicher Weise mit allen experimentellen Resultaten bis heute überein. Zweitens ist sie eine Theorie profunder mathematischer Schönheit. Das Einzige, das gegen sie gesagt werden kann, ist, dass sie absolut keinen Sinn macht!»

Das, was keinen Sinn macht, ist das ontologische Problem: Wo sind die Nussschalen, wenn es keinen Strand gibt? Es wurde von der Kopenhagener Schule pragmatisch beantwortet: Ohne Messung kein Photon. Das Einzige, wovon wir wissen, sind zeitliche und räumliche Koinzidenzen (Zeigerausschläge, Filmschwärzungen an bestimmten Orten und zu bestimmten Zeiten) und diese ergeben sich ganz exakt aufgrund der Theorie der Wahrscheinlichkeitswellen. Die Frage «Wo ist das Photon vor der Messung?» ist so unsinnig wie die Frage «Was war vor dem Anfang der Zeit?».

Diese extreme Sicht der Wirklichkeit stellt einen radikalen Gebrauch von Occams Messer dar – entia non sunt multiplicanda praeter necessitatem. Das Wegschneiden aller unnötigen Begriffe war vom Positivismus beeinflusst. Es drängt sich in diesem Zusammenhang der Gedanke an eine analoge Entwicklung in der Philosophie auf, die mit der Abschaffung des «Dings an sich» begann und schließlich zum subjektiven Idealismus führte. (Dieses Buch verschwindet, wenn ich die Augen schließe.)

Auf unser Beispiel übertragen heißt das in der Tat: ohne Strand keine Nussschalen. Es existiert nur eine Verteilung von Wahrscheinlichkeiten, welche im Augenblick der Beobachtung zusammenbricht – etwa wenn ein Bromsilberkorn im Film (dem Messgerät) durch ein beobachtetes Photon geschwärzt wird.

Nun wird es aber noch verwunderlicher: Bricht die Wahrscheinlichkeitswelle im Augenblick der Belichtung zusammen oder erst bei der Entwicklung des Films? Die Bromsilbermoleküle der Emulsion bestehen ja aus Atomen und diese wiederum sind Wahrscheinlichkeitswellen, wie die Quantenmechanik so erfolgreich gezeigt hatte. Bei der Belichtung kann also noch keine Rede davon sein, dass die Wahrscheinlichkeitswelle zusammenbricht – der Beobachter muss

schon draufschauen! Letztendlich gelten aber auch für die Entstehung des
Bildes auf der Netzhaut quantentheoretische Gesetze und auch die organischen
Zustände im Gehirn sind atomistisch geregelt – auch dort nur überlagerte
Wahrscheinlichkeiten. Erst das Bewusstsein des Beobachters kann aus dieser
Kette von Wahrscheinlichkeitswellen etwas Reales machen. Der Mathematiker
John von Neumann hat diese Theorie des Messens 1935 im Vollbesitz seiner
nicht unerheblichen geistigen Kräfte aufgestellt. Wir zitieren zur Erfrischung
aus seiner Arbeit: «[...] das Messen, bzw. der damit verknüpfte Vorgang der subjektiven Apperzeption [ist] eine gegenüber der physikalischen Umwelt neue,
auf diese nicht zurückführbare Wesenheit. Denn sie führt aus dieser hinaus oder
richtiger: sie führt hinein, in das unkontrollierbare [...] gedankliche Innenleben
des Individuums.»[7]

Die Katze

Auf den Punkt gebracht, lautet das Bekenntnis der Quantenmechanik: Der
Beobachter erzeugt die Welt – J. A. Wheeler spricht von der Beobachtung als
einem «elementaren Schöpfungsakt. Das Universum ist auf sonderbare Weise
ein Mitbestimmungsuniversum.»

Wie sehr dieser revoluzzerhafte Standpunkt unserem Verständnis der
Wirklichkeit zuwiderläuft, war schon dem Großvater von Schrödingers Katze
anzusehen. Im Jahr 1935 waren zwei Dinge klar: Erstens, dass die Quanten-
mechanik eine hervorragende Theorie ist, und zweitens, dass man wohl auf
absehbare Zeit mit den Eigentümlichkeiten der Theorie würde leben müssen.
Erwin Schrödinger selbst fasste die erkenntnistheoretischen Grundlagen der
Quantenmechanik in einem Aufsatz zusammen, dessen Titel «Die gegenwärtige
Situation in der Quantenmechanik» die Unzufriedenheit des Autors ahnen lässt.
(Dass diese Situation bis zum Ende des Jahrtausends anhalten sollte, hätte sich
Schrödinger nicht träumen lassen). In diesem Aufsatz erfindet er, um die eigen-
tümlichen Effekte der Quantenmechanik zu beleuchten, seine berühmt gewor-
dene Katze. Lassen wir ihn selbst zu Wort kommen:

«[...] Man kann aber auch ganz burleske Fälle konstruieren. Eine Katze
wird in eine Stahlkammer gesperrt, zusammen mit folgender Höllenmaschine
(die man gegen den direkten Zugriff der Katze sichern muss): In einem Geiger'schen Zählrohr befindet sich eine winzige Menge radioaktiver Substanz, so
wenig, dass im Laufe einer Stunde vielleicht eines ihrer Atome zerfällt, ebenso
wahrscheinlich aber auch keines; geschieht es, so spricht das Zählrohr an und
betätigt über ein Relais ein Hämmerchen, das ein Kölbchen mit Blausäure zer-
trümmert. Hat man dieses ganze System eine Stunde lang sich selbst überlassen,
so wird man sich sagen, dass die Katze noch lebt, wenn inzwischen kein Atom

zerfallen ist. Der erste Atomzerfall würde sie vergiftet haben. Die Psi-Funktion [Wahrscheinlichkeitswelle; Anm. des Autors] des ganzen Systems würde das so zum Ausdruck bringen, dass in ihr die lebende und die tote Katze [...] zu gleichen Teilen gemischt oder verschmiert sind [...]»
Es ist offensichtlich, dass Schrödinger damit sagen wollte: Überlegt euch etwas weniger Bescheuertes!

Der geneigte Leser wartet gespannt auf die Erlösung der halb toten Katze, denn dass da wo ein Hund begraben liegt, ist klar. Es sei bereits jetzt verraten, dass man ihn immer noch nicht gefunden hat, den Hund. Wir konnten inzwischen nur ein paar Hinweise sammeln.
Den ersten Hinweis findet man schon in unserer einfachen Teich-Nussschalen-Analogie. Erinnern wir uns, dass beim Entstehen einer Nussschale die gesamte Welle schlagartig zusammenbricht. Soll heißen, sobald am Punkt A des Ufers eine Nussschale entsteht, hat ein Beobachter am gegenüberliegenden Ufer, Punkt B, keine Chance mehr, eine solche zu finden, da die Wahrscheinlichkeitswelle mit der Messung am Punkt A überall verschwindet. Es sieht so aus, als würde das Ergebnis eines Experiments in Punkt A augenblicklich das beeinflussen, was in B geschehen kann – und damit ist die außersinnliche Wahrnehmung, die man durch Leugnen der Nussschalen vor der Messung aus-zusperren gehofft hatte, wieder da. Diese Idee hat Einstein 1935 mit zwei Mitarbeitern in einem berühmten Aufsatz mit dem Titel «Kann man die quanten-mechanische Beschreibung der Wirklichkeit als vollständig betrachten?» präzisiert. In der Arbeit wird gezeigt, dass, falls die Quantenmechanik stimmt, der Zustand von Teilchen B davon abhängt, was ich mit Teilchen A anstelle, und seien die beiden Lichtjahre voneinander entfernt. Dies war für Einstein so evi-dent unmöglich, dass die Prämisse falsch sein musste. Bohrs Antwort, unter demselben Titel erschienen, lautete sinngemäß: Es ist schon richtig, dass der Zustand von Teilchen B davon abhängt, was mit Teilchen A geschieht, aber dabei handelt es sich nicht um reale Zustände, sondern um Wahrscheinlich-keitswellen, also um Möglichkeiten, und diese Tatsache ist zwar erstaunlich, aber weder widersprüchlich noch paradox. Warum sollte also mit der Quanten-mechanik etwas nicht in Ordnung sein?

Die Nachkommenschaft

Es sollte 30 Jahre dauern, bis John Bell eine Antwort auf diese Frage fand, indem er Einsteins Gedankenexperiment erweiterte. Er zeigte zunächst, dass die Er-gebnisse von Experimenten mit Teilchen A und B einer bestimmten Beziehung, der Bell'schen Ungleichung, gehorchen müssen, wenn die Versuche an Teilchen

A keinen Einfluss auf die Ergebnisse von Versuchen an B haben. (Was wir still-
schweigend als selbstverständlich betrachten: Das Ergebnis von Würfel-
experimenten eines Beobachters beeinflusst nicht, was ein anderer, entfernter
Beobachter erwürfelt. Man bezeichnet diese Tatsache als die Separierbarkeit
der Welt.)[8] Dann zeigte Bell, dass die Quantenmechanik Versuchsergebnisse an
den beiden Teilchen voraussagt, welche die Bell'sche Ungleichung verletzen!
Damit war Folgendes klar:

– Entweder ist die Welt so aus einzelnen Bauklötzen aufgebaut und zerlegbar,
wie der kleine Maxi sich das vorstellt, und die Quantenmechanik ist falsch;
– oder die Quantenmechanik stimmt, und die Welt ist nicht separierbar, sondern wesentlich kompexer als wir dachten – alles hängt mit allem zusammen!

Der Wutanfall eines Cephalopoden von Alpha Centauri 6, der in sein Inter-
stellar-Video wieder mal nur «Dynasty» reinkriegt, könnte augenblicklich den
Ausgang eines Experimentes auf der Erde beeinflussen, bei dem eine gewisse
Katze und ein radioaktives Atom beteiligt sind.

Der Haken an der Sache war, dass im Jahr 1965, als Bell seine Ungleichung
fand, niemand die vorgeschlagenen Versuche durchführen konnte. Es scheiter-
te an technischen Kleinigkeiten, wie z. B. passende Wahrscheinlichkeitswellen
in genügender Menge herzustellen oder die richtige Pikosekunde für die
Messung zu wählen. So bot zwar Bells Ergebnis zwei faszinierende Alternativen,
aber keine Entscheidung. Es war etwas für Logiker, Ästheten und Mystiker. Von
den rechnenden und messenden Physikern wurde Bells Arbeit nicht einmal
ignoriert. Bis 1982 wusste man nicht, ob die Quantenmechanik falsch ist oder
extraterrestrische Wutanfälle tatsächlich eine Katze töten können. Dann legte
Alain Aspect experimentelle Beweise dafür vor, dass die Bell'sche Ungleichung
falsch ist;[9] somit ist die Quantenmechanik richtig und die Cephalopoden von
Alpha Centauri 6 können tatsächlich unser Leben beeinflussen.

Warum das so ist, wissen wir nicht. Die Entwicklung in der Quantentheorie,
wie wir sie beschrieben haben, hat neue und aufregende Einsichten in den
Mikrokosmos gebracht, aber wir können sie immer noch nicht richtig in ein
stimmiges Weltbild einordnen, wie das Richard Feynman, Nobelpreisträger für
Physik im Jahr 1965, ausdrückte: «I think I can safely say that nobody today
understands quantum mechanics.»
     Natürlich gab es sofort nach Bells Veröffentlichung Vorschläge für über-
lichtschnelle Kommunikation, was im Widerspruch zur Relativitätstheorie
stünde und der zentrale Punkt war, mit dem Einstein sich nie zufrieden geben
konnte.[10] Zum Glück stellt sich heraus, dass die Welt wenigstens diesbezüglich
in Ordnung ist. Nehmen wir an, dass Hinz an Kunz eine überlichtschnelle

Nachricht schicken will. Beide verwenden dazu ein Gerät, mit dem man die Polarisation von Lichtwellen messen kann, die von einer auf halbem Wege liegenden Quelle in zwei Richtungen abgestrahlt werden. Kunz richtet sein Messgerät waagrecht aus. Ein Photon wird nun in dieser Polarisationsebene entweder registriert oder nicht registriert. Kunz empfängt also einen Binärcode aus Nullen und Einsen. Hinz kann sein Gerät senkrecht oder waagrecht ausrichten, und tatsächlich hängt die von Kunz empfangene Signalfolge davon ab, wie Hinz sein Gerät ausgerichtet hat![1] Auf diese Art kann Hinz den von Kunz empfangenen Code instantan beeinflussen – aber kann er ihm eine Nachricht schicken?

Erinnern wir uns, dass die empfangenen Lichtwellen «Wahrscheinlichkeitswellen» sind, die Photonen also regellos daherkommen – Kunz empfängt eine Zufallsfolge. Der empfangene Binärcode könnte so aussehen:

	Hinz waagrecht	Hinz senkrecht
Hinz	10110100I	10110100I
Kunz	10110100I	01001010

Wir sehen, dass im ersten Fall Kunz immer dann eine Eins empfängt, wenn Hinz auch eine Eins feststellt, während es im zweiten Fall umgekehrt ist (einsichtig, da die beiden Photonen gleiche Polarisationsrichtung haben, was bei diesem Versuchsaufbau der Fall ist); die von Kunz empfangene Zahlenfolge hängt also tatsächlich davon ab, was Hinz tut! Aber wie auch immer Hinz sein Gerät positioniert, Kunz empfängt eine Zufallsfolge von Nullen und Einsen. Genauer gesagt empfängt Kunz verschiedene Zufallsfolgen, je nachdem, wie Hinz sein Gerät einstellt, kann aber damit aus dem einfachen Grund nichts anfangen, weil die Aneinanderreihung von Nullen und Einsen in seiner Nachricht eben zufällig ist. Der Einfluss von Hinzens Entscheidung, sein Messgerät waagrecht oder senkrecht zu stellen, auf Kunzens Messergebnis äußert sich bloß in der Korrelation der beiden Zufallsfolgen; 1 bei waagrecht, -1 bei senkrecht. Die mysteriöse überlichtschnelle Beeinflussung können die beiden also erst feststellen, wenn sie ihre Binärcodes vergleichen, und dazu müssten sie einander treffen oder zumindest anrufen – offensichtlich immer noch die beste Methode, Information weiterzugeben. Man könnte sagen, die Natur kommuniziert überlichtschnell, verwehrt es uns aber durch die Einführung des Zufalls.[2]

Es ist verfrüht, nun die Schultern zu heben und zur Tagesordnung überzugehen. Immerhin gibt es einen ernst zu nehmenden Vorschlag, mit Hilfe des beschriebenen Effekts eine absolut abhörsichere Signalstrecke einzurichten[3] – ein heimlicher Lauscher würde die empfangene Nachricht beeinflussen und instantan zerstören – und es muss eingeräumt werden, dass die Nichtseparierbarkeit der Welt bei makroskopischen Quanteneffekten, wie z. B. bei der Supraleitung, Bedeutung erlangen kann.

Es ist aber genauso wenig angebracht, nun einem mystischen Holismus zu verfallen, da alles mit allem zusammenhängt, sich alles in allem äußert. Fast meint man, die Natur habe uns, um uns an der Nutzung dieses wunderbaren Allzusammenhangs zu hindern, eine lange Nase gedreht, indem sie den quantenmechanischen Zufall erfunden hat. Es ist durchaus möglich, dass alles mit allem zusammenhängt, aber es äußert sich eben nicht.

Und so mag es sein, dass du, Leser, diesen Aufsatz nur aufgrund eines allumfassenden, geheimnisvollen Impulses gekauft hast, der das Universum erfüllte, als ich dies schrieb – ein anderer aber hat ihn gerade deshalb eben nicht gelesen.

ANMERKUNGEN:

1) Anton Zeilinger und seine Arbeitsgruppe an der Universität Wien haben erheblichen Anteil an diesen Entwicklungen. Siehe z. B. A. Zeilinger, Quantum Teleportation. Scientific American (April 2000), 32.

2) W. Heisenberg, Z. Phys. 43, 172 (1927)

3) Natürlich führt das zu Pannen, wie das Intermezzo mit der kalten Kernfusion gezeigt hat.

4) E. P. Wigner, Remarks in the Mind-Body Question, in I. J. Good (Hrsg.): The Scientist speculates, Basic Books, New York 1962

5) Eine dritte Alternative ist als Theorie der Führungswellen bekannt. Ursprünglich von Einstein als «Gespensterfeld» (sic!) vorgeschlagen, sollte die Welle den korpuskularen Quanten den Weg weisen, ohne selbst physikalische Realität zu haben. Diese Variante, von DeBroglie kurzzeitig weiterverfolgt, hatte aber nie eine Chance gegen die mächtige Kopenhagener Deutung. 1950 griff David Bohm die Idee in abgewandelter Form wieder auf, aber die rechnerischen Erfolge der etablierten Theorie waren so groß, dass aus den Führungswellen nichts wurde. Nach Bells Entdeckung 1964 (siehe später im Text) stieg das Interesse an jenem archaischen Zugang, und heute sind immerhin einige wenige Wissenschaftler, die eher als Epistemologen denn als Physiker bezeichnet werden sollten, bereit, Alternativen zur Kopenhagen Deutung zu diskutieren.

6) Zitat aus F. Bloch, Physics Today, Dec. 1976, p24

7) J. von Neumann, Mathematische Grundlagen der Quantenmechanik, Springer, Berlin 1932
Die Passage erinnert weniger an ein Mathematik-Lehrbuch als vielmehr an einen Abschnitt aus einer philosophischen Abhandlung zum Ich-Problem. Wie sehr Physik und Philosophie miteinander verschmelzen, erkennt man an Aufsätzen wie «Existence of free will as a problem of physics» in seriösen Fachzeitschriften. Allerdings ist das Publizieren in Fachzeitschriften oder das Auftreten bekannter Namen in der Autorenzeile kein Garant dafür, dass die Arbeit seriös ist. So wurde z. B. 1974 auf Anregung Arthur Köstlers eine Konferenz über Quantenmechanik (QM) abgehalten, an der weltbekannte Physiker und weniger bekannte Parapsychologen teilnahmen. Der Konferenzband enthält unter anderem Zweifelhaften einen Beitrag von H. Puthoff und R. Targ, die, als Uri Geller en vogue war, dessen hellseherische Fähigkeiten «bewiesen» hatten. Daraus sollte man nicht schließen, dass Geller nicht hellsehen kann oder dass QM nichts mit unerklärten Phänomenen zu tun hat. Aber zwei andere Dinge werden dadurch ins rechte Licht gerückt. Erstens: Die Parapsychologie verhält sich zur QM wie Uri Geller zu bewiesenem Hellsehen; und zweitens: Das Verlangen nach den hermetischen Wissenschaften ist so stark, dass die Kritikfähigkeit auch kritischer Geister paralysiert wird (es müsste also richtig Paralysologie und nicht Parapsychologie heißen) und dass Pseudo-Wissenschaftliches, Pseudo-

Fantastisches eine Wissenschaft infiltrieren kann, die ohnehin schon fantastisch genug ist. Nebenbemerkung: Es gibt etwa zehnmal so viel Astrologen wie Astronomen.

8) Hier ist im Gegensatz zu Einsteins Gedankenexperiment nicht mehr von Wahrscheinlichkeitswellen, sondern von Versuchsergebnissen (Filmschwärzungen, Zeigerausschlägen) die Rede, sodass Bohrs Einwand nicht mehr greifen würde.

9) Genauer: Bis 1982 wurden 7 Experimente durchgeführt, teils mit Elektronen, teils mit Photonen. Die älteren Messungen lieferten widersprüchliche Resultate wegen der geringen Messgenauigkeit. Erst Aspects Experiment brachte Sicherheit.

10) Wenn überlichtschnelle Kommunikation möglich wäre, könnten Signale in die Vergangenheit geschickt werden, was beträchtliche Turbulenzen auslösen würde. Man denke nur an die Möglichkeiten an der Börse. Eine schöne Darstellung ist: G. A. Benford, D. L. Book, and W. A. Newcomb, The Tachyonic Antitelephone, Physical Review, D 2 (1970): 263–265

11) Diese erstaunliche Beeinflussung ist bereits in unserer einfachen Analogie (Wasserwellen im Teich) zu erkennen. Dazu brauchen wir nur jene Teile der

Welle betrachten, die von der Mitte zu gegenüberliegenden Ufern laufen. Sobald an einem Punkt des Ufers gemessen wird, entsteht eine Nussschale, und die Welle bricht auch am gegenüberliegenden Punkt zusammen.

12) Das Experiment ist hier des Verständnisses wegen vereinfacht dargestellt. Das beschriebene Ergebnis könnte auch mit der Annahme erklärt werden, dass von der Lichtquelle nicht Wahrscheinlichkeitswellen, sondern Photonen emittiert werden. Erst wenn Hinz eine Position zwischen senkrecht und waagrecht wählt, sind die experimentell verifizierten Ergebnisse nur mehr durch die Quantenmechanik beschreibbar – die zusammenbrechende Wahrscheinlichkeitswelle sorgt dafür, dass Hinzens Entscheidung das Messergebnis am anderen Ende der Signalstrecke augenblicklich beeinflusst. Wenn die hier im Zeitraffer dargestellte Geschichte eines Problems, die sich über nahezu ein Jahrhundert erstreckte, etwas zeigt, dann die Tatsache, dass Begriffe, die wir für feststehend und klar hielten (wie Ort, Separierbarkeit, Informationsübertragung und Wahrscheinlichkeit), lax und verschwommen sind.

13) Zitiert nach: Scientific American, Mai 1989, p20. Inzwischen (2004) gibt es solche Signalstrecken, die über einige km Distanz funktionieren.

Seite 76

Der Fall Eleonore Zugun

——— –

von men on the moon

——— –

Synopsis

Im Winter 1925 ging die zwölfjährige Eleonore Zugun mit ihrem älteren Cousin im hintersten Winkel Rumäniens durch einen Wald. Sie wollte ihre blinde Urgroßmutter besuchen, die im nächsten Dorf lebte. Das Mädchen fand auf dem Weg eine Münze und nahm sie an sich, obwohl ihr Cousin sie warnte, da im Wald gefundenes Geld nach einem rumänischen Aberglauben Teufelsgeld sei. Eleonore behielt die Münze dennoch und gab sie im Dorf für Süßigkeiten aus. Sie teilte diese auch nicht mit ihrer Cousine, die bei der Urgroßmutter wohnte. Darüber verärgert sagte die alte Frau, dass das Mädchen den Teufel «mitgefressen» habe. Er sei nun in ihrem Körper und werde sie nie mehr verlassen.

Diese Worte wirkten auf Eleonore wie ein Fluch: Bereits am nächsten Tag wurden wie von Geisterhand Steine in das Haus geworfen und Gegenstände in der Nähe des Mädchens bewegt und in die Luft gehoben. Als Eleonore in ihr Heimatdorf zurückgeschickt wurde, traten diese Phänomene nach einer Pause von drei Tagen auch dort auf. Später kam noch hinzu, dass sie von unsichtbaren Kräften bespuckt wurde und Kratzer im Gesicht aufwies. Schnell nannten die Menschen in Talpa sie «das Teufelsmädchen».

Die mysteriösen Ereignisse verbreiteten sich wie ein Lauffeuer im ganzen Land. Auch an Erscheinungen dieser Art besonders interessierte Kreise bekamen bald von dem Fall mit anscheinend poltergeistartigen Manifestationen Wind. So auch Gräfin Wassilko aus Wien, deren Familie ursprünglich aus Rumänien stammte. Als die zu diesem Zeitpunkt dreißigjährige Gräfin, die sich seit langem für mediale Phänomene interessierte, von einem Spukfall auf «ihrem eigenen» Grund und Boden hörte, reiste sie dorthin. Nach ersten Beobachtungen ließ sie Eleonore zu sich nach Wien holen, um ihren Fall gründlich untersuchen zu können.

Schon am Tag nach ihrer Ankunft sah ein Dienstmädchen, wie ein Silberlöffel ohne äußere Einwirkung vom Tisch fiel. Von da an hielt die Gräfin alle Phänomene um Eleonore in protokollarischen Aufzeichnungen fest. Sie konnte dabei zwei Phasen unterscheiden, denn nach einem halben Jahr gingen die Ortsveränderungen von Gegenständen in Hautphänomene über – Kratzer und Bisse auf der Haut sowie das Bespucken des Mädchens durch unsichtbare Kräfte.

Kurz darauf begab sich die Gräfin mit Eleonore auf eine fünfmonatige «Tournee», um in London, Berlin, Nürnberg und München führende Parapsychologen zu besuchen. Während dieser Reise führten verschiedene Zeugen Aufzeichnungen, an ihrem Ende entstand ein dokumentarischer Film über die dermographischen Auffälligkeiten an Eleonores Körper.

Bei seiner Rückkehr nach Wien bekam das Mädchen seine erste Regelblutung. Die Phänomene wurden schlagartig seltener und verschwanden kurz darauf völlig. Eleonore verbrachte noch ein Jahr in Wien und kehrte anschließend nach Rumänien zurück, wo sie ein ruhiges Leben ohne weitere mysteriöse Phänomene führte.

Wissenschaftliche Randbemerkungen von Prof. Peter Mulacz

Die in Anwesenheit von Eleonore Zugun aufgetretenen «Poltergeist»-Phänomene begannen mit unerklärlichen Bewegungen verschiedener Objekte. So wurden von einer unsichtbaren Kraft aus einem nahe gelegenen Fluss Steine in das Haus geworfen. Als Beobachter die Steine markierten und zum Fluss zurücktrugen, tauchten diese wenig später wieder im Haus auf. Niemand konnte feststellen, wie sie die Distanz von 80 Metern überwanden.

Die abergläubische Landbevölkerung hat diese Phänomene dem Teufel – rumänisch: «Dracu» – zugeschrieben. Von Bedeutung ist dabei, dass der Cousin gegenüber Eleonore von «Teufelsgeld» sprach und die Urgroßmutter fluchartig äußerte, das Mädchen habe mit ihren Süßigkeiten den Teufel «mitgefressen». Der «Dracu» wurde dadurch zu einer Personifikation in Eleonores Unbewusstem, zu einer Spaltpersönlichkeit. Zusätzlich wurde Eleonore mit einem starken Schuldkomplex beladen, wie psychoanalytische Untersuchungen später ergaben.

In Wien waren die Phänomene um Eleonore weit weniger heftig als in ihrer Heimat. Einzig kleinere Gegenstände verschwanden und tauchten dann anderswo wieder auf oder bewegten sich, als ob sie lebendig wären. Die Wurfrichtung verlief dabei interessanterweise immer zu dem Mädchen hin, was als autoaggressiver Akt im Zusammenhang mit seinem Schuldkomplex zu deuten ist.

In der zweiten Phase von Eleonores Medialität rückten zunehmend dermographische Phänomene in den Vordergrund. Das Mädchen litt zufällig an einer häufig auftretenden Überreaktion der Haut: Minimale Wunden von Kratz- und Bissspuren im Gesicht, am Nacken, Dekolletee sowie an den Armen schwollen binnen Minuten quaddelartig an. Im Gegensatz zu religiös motivierten Stigmata entstanden diese Wunden jedoch nicht in der Tiefe des Gewebes, sondern auf der Oberfläche der Haut. Dieser Prozess war bei Eleonore also kein rein psychosomatischer, da er einen Umweg über die «Außenwelt» nahm, was der eigentliche Kern der Psychokinese ist.

Gräfin Wassilkos fünfmonatige «Tournee» mit Eleonore mag für heutige Ohren nach Wanderzirkus klingen. Allerdings erschien sie wichtig, um ein starkes Medium einer Reihe hoch qualifizierter und voneinander unabhängiger Forscher vorzuführen. Dadurch hat der Fall ein hohes Maß öffentlicher Evidenz gewonnen, wie es erst mehr als dreißig Jahre später im Fall Rosenheim wieder gelingen sollte. Zum Abschluss der Untersuchungen wurde Anfang 1927 von der Firma EMELKA in München ein Film aufgenommen, der einen der ersten Fälle filmischer Dokumentation auf dem Gebiet der Parapsychologie darstellt. In der Folge enstand um die Kern-Beobachtergruppe die «Österreichische Gesellschaft für Psychische Forschung» (heute «Österreichische Gesellschaft für Parapsychologie und Grenzbereiche der Wissenschaften»).

Seite 132

Im Verein der Tonbandstimmenforscher

———   –

Eine Dokumentation von Ernst Schmiederer mit Fotos von Thomas Smetana

———   –

Ein Besuch im Vereinslokal in der Wiener Eisvogelgasse. Dienstagabend. Ein
Tisch, Kaffeetassen, ein Aschenbecher. Zwei Frauen lesen Transkripte einer
Tonbandeinspielung. Parallel dazu spielen sie auf einem Walkman immer wieder
eine einzige sekundenkurze Passage der Aufnahme ab: Stimmfetzen sind da zu
hören, Fremdsprachen, das Frequenzrauschen eines Radios. Sonst, so glaubt der
Besucher, nichts. Die beiden Frauen hören mehr.
«Der Rudi. Haben Sie das gehört? Das ist der Rudi.» Die Stimme, die kurz
zu hören ist, ordnen die beiden Frauen dem Mann der einen zu, dem Rudi eben.
Rudis Witwe sagt: «Na, ist das deutlich? Im Jänner sind es drei Jahre seit der
Rudi gestorben ist. Aber haben Sie das gehört: Der Rudi. Mir ist ganz kalt ge-
worden, als ich das gehört hab, eine Gänsehaut hab ich bekommen. Der Rudi.»

Maria Manov, die Obfrau

Wir treffen uns hier jeden Dienstag. Um sechs am Abend. Locker, mit einem
Kaffee. Aber um sieben Uhr, pünktlich, geht es los: Wir sind eingespeichert als
die um sieben Uhr beginnende Gruppe. Die Gruppe Wien ist 19 Uhr Dienstag.
Das wissen die drüben. Ihr seid aber spät, hören wir manchmal.
    Nun aber der Reihe nach. Ich bin eine geborene Stacher, stamme also aus
einer Lehrer- und Arztfamilie. Wir haben zwei Universitätsprofessoren der
Medizin in der Familie. Mein Mann war Opernsänger, Solist. Zum Schluss hat
er ein eigenes Ensemble gehabt, wo er nur orthodoxe Kirchenmusik gemacht
hat, wunderschön. Orthodox, das ist östlich, mein Mann war aus Bulgarien.
1995 ist er gestorben. Ganz schnell. Der war in drei Wochen weg. Und da wird
man nachdenklich, überlegt, irgendwas muss da ja noch sein. Zumal ich in den
70er Jahren schon Kontakt mit einem bulgarischen Medium gehabt habe. Mit
einer blinden Frau. Ein ausgezeichnetes Medium.
    Jedenfalls war ich im November 1995 auf einem Transkommunikations-
kongress, wo es um Tonbandstimmen ging, aber auch um Medien, Computer-

mitteilungen, Fernsehvideobilder. Alles. Da waren wirklich große Leute dort, unter anderem der Professor Senkowski. Dessen Buch habe ich studiert. Nach und nach habe ich Bekanntschaften gemacht, im deutschen Forscherkreis. Sehr nette Treffen sind da zustande gekommen. Bis nach Ägypten sind wir gefahren, wo wir in der Großen Pyramide eingespielt haben. Sehr schöne Sachen. Irgendwann habe ich mich hingesetzt und selbst bestimmte Wesenheiten gerufen. Und siehe da, ich hab die auf Tonband gekriegt. Den Pfarrer Leo Schmidt zum Beispiel. Der sagt da: «Schmidt, höre Tote.» Das war sein geflügeltes Wort: Schmidt, höre Tote. Den Herrn Manfred Boden, Charly haben sie ihn genannt, der sehr viel auf dem Gebiet gearbeitet hat, von dem habe ich auch Antwort gekriegt. Vom Peter Härting, der ist der Mann von einer sehr lieben Freundin. Der Friedrich Jürgenson hat sich gemeldet, der Pionier der Tonbandstimmenforschung. Der Doktor Konstantin Raudive. Ich hab die alle auf Band. Packlweise habe ich Tonbänder und Aufzeichnungen, von Einstein bis Chruschtschow.

Auch mein Mann hat sich gemeldet. Er hat mir gesagt, dass die ersten Male jemand für ihn geantwortet habe. Offensichtlich konnte er das damals noch nicht. Es ist technisch sehr schwer, die Jenseitigen müssen nämlich in diese so genannte Voice Box reden, damit das bei uns ankommt. Und das kann nicht jeder. Daher redet oft jemand stellvertretend für sie.

Das Erste, was mein Mann mir gesagt hat, war Folgendes: «Freut mich, Wahnsinn, die Tatsache mit dir.» Gemeint hat er die Tatsache, dass wir Kontakt haben. Da hat er gewusst, ich weiß von ihm und er weiß von mir. Das ist ein Trost. Dann ist einmal reingekommen: «Weine nicht, ich lebe.» Dann: «CHier Manov», mit dem slawischen CHier Manov, da erkennen Sie, dass er das ist. «Ich säh euch» – das offene ä. Da ist es allen bulgarischen Freunden, denen ich dieses Tonband vorgespielt hab, kalt runtergelaufen.

Irgendwann geht das weiter. Man will wissen, wer der Schutzgeist ist, der Geistführer. Man hört so Sachen: «Maria, du solltest beten, Maria, du betest gar nicht in der Früh, Maria, tu beten. Maria, Gott liebt dich richtig.» Oder: «Der Adonä richtig liebt dich, guter Gott, liebt er dich von Herzen.» Das ist überreligiös. «Auch der Koran sei betätigt.» So hat sich ein Ali gemeldet. Ich hab ja nicht gewusst, wer der Ali ist. Aber dann hab ich gelernt, das war der Schwiegersohn des Propheten. «Auch der Koran sei betätigt.»

Ich selbst bin Katholikin. An und für sich brauchte ich gar keine Religion. Denn es stellt sich mit dieser Arbeit ja die Frage, wer oder was ist Gott? Gott ist alles, was ist. Alles. Und die Jenseitigen, das sind unsere, die hier auf der Erde waren und verstorben sind. Wir kriegen von den Jenseitigen Ratschläge. Und weder sie noch wir wollen, dass man das an die große Glocke hängt.

Maximilian Kvacsik, der Toningenieur

Schauen Sie, hier haben wir einen Kurzwellenempfänger. Es geht darum, dass man ausländisches Trägermaterial hat, Jugoslawisch, Russisch, was Beständiges soll es jedenfalls sein. Ich muss dabei zwischen den Sendern wechseln, sodass ich nur Sprache habe, ich will ja die Musik nicht draufhaben. Hier haben wir ein normales Aufnahmegerät, ein Kassettendeck. Dazu ein Wiedergabegerät. Das ist in unserem Fall ein umgebautes Autoradio. Sie werden fragen, warum ein altes Autoradio? Nun, es hat eine robustere Mechanik und ist speziell für unseren Zweck umgebaut.

Schließlich brauchen wir, für die Unterbrechung des Trägergemisches, einen Zeitschalter, damit wir jeweils 5 Sekunden von einem Sender bekommen. Da unten steht noch der so genannte Tremolant, auf dem man von einem Hertz bis 25 Hertz modulieren kann. Das kennen Sie ja aus der Musik, den Lesly-Effekt, das Tremolo der Gitarristen.

Das ist alles.

Wir strahlen nun das Trägermaterial, die ausländischen Radiosender also, in den Raum ab. Und die Leute stellen ihre Fragen. Das Ganze wird aufgenommen. Und nachdem alle fertig sind mit ihren Fragen, wird es wiedergegeben. Und dann sollte was drauf sein.

Anton Rosenberger, der Hinterbliebene

Ich verdanke dem Verein hier wirklich alles. Besonders unserer Frau Manov. Sie sagt mir alles, was auf den Tonbändern zu hören ist, weil ich selbst ja nicht mehr so gut höre.

Durch Zufall bin ich dazugekommen. Mein Bruder hat mich eines Tages angerufen: «Toni, dreh den Fernseher auf, da gibt es eine Sendung, da sagt jemand, es gibt ein Leben nach dem Tod.» Nun, das war ein Film über diesen, über unseren Verein.

Als ich das erste Mal herkam, wurde mir erklärt, dass dieser Verein gegründet wurde, um jenen Menschen zu helfen, die einen lieben Menschen verloren haben. Und ich gehöre zu diesen Menschen. Ich hab eine sehr, sehr glückliche Ehe geführt. War 47 Jahre verheiratet. Dann kommt plötzlich eine Krankheit. Meine Frau hat Krebs gehabt, leider Gottes, einen sehr schwierigen. Daran ist sie gestorben. Und ich war total fertig, wollte mir das Leben nehmen.

Durch reinen Zufall ... obwohl, es gibt ja keine Zufälle ... also, ich wurde hierher geführt. Leider habe ich beim ersten Versuch, mit meiner Frau Kontakt aufzunehmen, keine Antwort bekommen. Da ist eine sehr liebe Frau zu mir gekommen und hat gesagt: «Herr Rosenberger, bitte weinen Sie nicht. Man wird

Ihrer Frau ausrichten, dass Sie gerufen haben und sie wird das nächste Mal anwesend sein.» Ich hab mich schon gefreut auf nächsten Dienstag und das nächste Mal war sie anwesend.

Ich habe meine Fragen gestellt: «Bitte gib mir eine Botschaft. Ich umarme
und küsse dich, dein Toni.»

Und sie hat geantwortet: «Anton, mein Geliebter, ich liebe dich.»
Da hab ich mir gedacht, ja, das kann jede sagen. Aber dann sagte sie noch:
«Toni, Mary, Nachricht.» Das sollte heißen: Toni, sag der Mary, das war ihre
Schwester, sag der Mary, dass ich lebe. Na, ich war ganz weg. Das weiß hier ja
niemand, mit der Mary.

Dann hat es andere Sachen gegeben, wo ich gefragt habe, bitte, kannst du
mir helfen, ich leide sehr an Sodbrennen. Und sie hat mir ein Mittel genannt.
Ich bin in die Apotheke gegangen und dort hat man mir gesagt: Das ist ein
Medikament gegen Sodbrennen. Ist das nicht umwerfend? Sie hat auch einmal
gesagt: «Toni, du hörst schlecht, du brauchst Hörhilfe.» Am nächsten Tag hat
mir der Arzt ein Hörgerät verschrieben.

Ich fühle mich wirklich sehr gesund heute und sehr wohl. Ich bin wieder
ein Mensch geworden, hab wieder Freude am Leben. So wäre das nicht weiter-
gegangen mit mir, wenn man da wach wird in der Früh und das Bett neben
einem ist leer, furchtbar, so was möchte ich nie mehr erleben. Aber jetzt weiß
ich, meine Frau wartet auf mich, das sagt sie mir des Öfteren. Und daher glaube
ich daran.

Eduard und Edith Köckeis, der Pionier und sein Schatten

Ich mach das seit 1978, da war hier noch gar kein Verein. Es gab eine kleine
Gruppe mit dem Ingenieur Seidl, jeden Montag im Kaffeehaus in der Stadt. Da
waren Techniker dabei, die Geräte gebastelt haben. Da hab ich den Herrn
Luksch kennen gelernt, der lange Zeit Obmann war. Dann ist der Kreis immer
größer geworden. Wir haben begonnen mit Einspielungen in Extrazimmern, da
waren oft 40 Leute dabei. Separat haben wir einen kleineren Kreis gemacht, mit
verschiedenen Methoden und Geräten haben wir da Versuche gemacht. Der
Kreis ist immer größer geworden. Der Herr Ingenieur Seidl wollte nicht, dass
ein Verein gegründet wird. Der Herr Luksch aber wollte den Verein, damit wir
Geräte irgendwo aufstellen können.

Heute wird ja nicht mehr geforscht. Wir haben in einer kleinen Gruppe
Fragen gestellt, mit einem Konzept. Der Herr Luksch hat, wenn er gelesen
hat in der Zeitung, es ist ein Mord geschehen, hat der Herr Luksch versucht,
den Mörder zu finden, Fragen zu stellen. Und hat diese Liste bei einem Rechts-
anwalt hinterlassen. Von zehn Mordfällen hat er in sieben den Namen des

Mörders am Band gehabt. Aber die Polizei hat sich da weniger interessiert. Er hat das dann aufgegeben, denn er wollte ja nur belegen, dass das Phänomen Tonbandstimmen existiert. Der Kreis ist kleiner geworden seit damals. Das Interesse lässt nach. Damals waren noch Junge dabei, jetzt eigentlich nicht mehr. Für mich war es früher interessanter, das Technische.

Ich hab begonnen mit einem normalen Spulentonbandgerät, dazu ein ganz normales Mikrofon ohne Verstärker. Damit hab ich gute Ergebnisse gehabt – die Senta Morina, die Sekretärin vom Doktor Raudive, hat sich gemeldet bei mir als Vermittlerin. Die Frau war gelähmt, im Rollstuhl, ist gestorben und ich habe Verbindung gekriegt mit ihr. Das ist ein halbes Jahr lang gegangen.

Heute haben wir Verstärker, da sind die Stimmen etwas stärker auszunehmen. Die Geräte sind besser, der Empfang. Aber die Stimmen werden nicht besser. Ich glaub, die Technik spielt überhaupt keine Rolle. Das sind Energien, die eine Rolle spielen, nicht die Technik.

Ich hab dann so meine Erlebnisse gehabt, im Lauf der Zeit, wie meine Frau gestorben ist, wir (Herr Köckeis zeigt auf Edith, seine zweite Frau) haben ja erst vor kurzem geheiratet, vor drei Jahren.

Ich hab selber Versuche gemacht, wie meine Frau gestorben ist. Ich hab mir erhofft, dass ich einige Mitteilungen bekommen werde. Das ist aber leider nicht eingetroffen. Ich hab wohl ihren Namen gekriegt, hab Kontakt bekommen, was eindeutig nur sie gewesen sein kann, weil niemand weiß das, was so persönlich Bezug nimmt.

Aber sonst habe ich von meiner Frau nichts Wesentliches mehr gekriegt, nicht was für mich von Interesse wäre, nur so: «Hast a Angst, ich steh hinter dir.» Zuletzt hab ich gehört: «Du kannst sie nicht erreichen, sie ist auf einer anderen Ebene, in eine andere Dimension übergegangen.» Es gibt ja verschiedene Ebenen im Jenseits.

(Herr Rosenberger schaltet sich ein:) Es gibt den Vorraum des Himmels, angeblich gibt es sieben Dimensionen, meine Frau dürfte in der dritten sein. Da sind die meisten, jedenfalls die, die anständig gelebt haben. Sie werden sich immer weiterbilden, sie lernen oben. Das wissen wir von Tonbandstimmenforschern.

(Herr Köckeis setzt fort:) Ich hab die Stimmen aufgezeichnet, aber in den letzten Jahren nichts mehr gemacht. Ich komme hierher, aber sonst mache ich nichts mehr. Die Sammlung habe ich in einem Studio zuhause, da hab ich so Boxen, da ist das eingeordnet.

(Frau Köckeis erklärt:) Wir fahren aus Sollenau mit der Südbahn hierher. Jeden Dienstag. Ich bin meinem Mann zuliebe hier. Er hat mir erzählt, was er da macht. Ich hab mir nur gedacht, ich geh mit, hör mir das an. Und jetzt sitze ich immer rückwärts und höre mir das an. Ich sage zu ihm, mach das, das ist in Ordnung. Ich selber, ich rufe nicht, nie. Mein Mann, der Erich, ist auch vor zehn Jahren gestorben. Da hat man mir gesagt: «Du darfst nicht so viel nachdenken, du musst loslassen, dann wird es dir auch besser gehen.» An das hab ich mich bis heute gehalten, darum rufe ich ihn nicht. Ich glaube, er will seine Ruhe haben und er soll sie haben. Ich muss Ihnen jetzt was sagen: Wenn er haben will, dass ich ihn ruf, dann müsst schon was von ihm kommen. Ehrlich gesagt wär mir das auch nicht ganz unrecht. Aber es kommt eben nichts. Daher ruf ich ihn auch nicht. Ich hab einen Namen, den weiß eigentlich niemand, außer meinem Mann jetzt, und dem Erich. Aber den Namen hör ich nicht, den müsst ich hören, dass ich weiß, er will gerufen werden.

(Herr Köckeis setzt fort:) Heute hab ich den Herrn Luksch gerufen und ihn gefragt, warum er sich nicht meldet. Er hat ja immer wieder erwähnt, wenn ich einmal drüben bin, ich werde mich melden und euch weiterhelfen. Aber bisher ist nichts durchgekommen. Seit 1991 oder 92 ist er tot. Aber alles, was wir bis jetzt von ihm gehört haben, war unwesentlich.

Darko und Xenia Horwat, die Eltern

Herr Horwat: Es ist sehr wichtig, dass man positive Energie hat. Ohne positive Energie klappt es überhaupt nicht. Die Technik ist an und für sich bedeutungslos. Es ist gut, wenn man ein Tonbandgerät hat, mit dem man repetieren kann, das ist wichtig beim Abhören. Normalerweise versteht man beim ersten Mal nichts, dann muss man zwei bis drei Mal abhören, dann versteht man die Stimme. Das, was mich interessiert, sind nicht die Hauptstimmen, sondern die Nebengeräusche. MP3 wird zu komprimiert, da verlieren sich die Nebenstimmen. Ich habe schlechte Erfahrungen mit MP3, wird zu stark komprimiert, ist nicht geeignet. Ich habe ein ganz gewöhnliches Philips-Gerät für 100 Euro. Das hat sich bewährt. Philips D 64.
 Es gibt mehrere Methoden. Für Anfänger ist es gut, wenn man einen Träger nimmt, der in einer Fremdsprache sendet. Die deutsche Sprache ist nicht geeignet, weil das ablenkt. Eine Sprache, die man nicht kennt, ist am besten geeignet. In den Pausen – man muss den Rhythmus dieser Sprache kennen, um die Pausen zu bestimmen – in den Pausen hört man dann Stimmen. Man läuft immer wieder Gefahr, dass man in Fremdsprache was erkennt, was nicht die Meldung ist.
 Seit zweieinhalb Jahren sind wir dabei, nach dem Tod unseres Sohnes. Er war 19 Jahre alt, da ist er gestorben. Er hat uns als Erbe ein Wort gelassen, und

das war: Hyperraum. Wir haben ein Buch gekauft und dort über Hyperraum gelesen. Dann haben wir Professor Mecklenburg in Deutschland kontaktiert und er hat uns mit Herrn Senkoswski in Kontakt gebracht. Und der hat mir dann gesagt, dass es einen Verein gibt. Beim ersten Mal war noch der zweite Sohn dabei. Unser Sohn im Jenseits hat ihn mit Chat-Internet-Namen angesprochen – den wusste ja sonst keiner. Hyperraum. Ich werde bald sterben und ich werde im Hyperraum sein. Er hat gewusst, dass er stirbt. Durch eine Gehirnblutung ist er gestorben.

Frau Horwat: Darf ich kurz unterbrechen. Mein Sohn hat gewusst, dass er stirbt. Ein Jahr vor seinem Tod hat er gefragt: «Mami, was ist der Sinn des Lebens?» Ich habe nicht antworten können. Er hat gesagt: «Jetzt hör mir gut zu. In einem Jahr werde ich sterben, bitte sei nicht traurig, ich werde dann mehr mit dir sein als heutzutage, ich bin dann im Hyperraum.» Das war das ausschlagende Wort. Was das bedeutet, hab ich damals nicht gewusst. Nach einem Jahr stirbt er wirklich. Er hat auch gesagt: «Mami, wir irren uns nicht, nach einem Jahr werde ich gehen.» Und tatsächlich: Am Tag vor Weihnachten haben wir gesprochen und einen Tag vor Weihnachten ist er gestorben.

Und sein erster Satz, mit dem er sich gemeldet hat, war: «Ich lebe.» Gestorben ist er am Tag vor Weihnachten 1999. Im März 2000 hab ich ihn zum ersten Mal gehört: «Ich lebe.»

Seite 268

Monsterwasser

—––   –

Eine Erzählung von Ernst Molden mit Illustrationen von Silja Götz

—––   –

I. Zeitungsmeldung

M.-See, Österreich. Haben die Alpen jetzt ihr Loch Ness? Am österreichischen M.-See jedenfalls bemerkten gleich fünf Zeugen dieselbe unglaubliche zoologische Erscheinung. An einer stark verengten Stelle des Gewässers, so die überraschend deckungsgleichen Angaben der Augenzeugen, sei ein mindestens sieben Meter langes Tier aus dem Wasser aufgetaucht, eine Art Weichschildkröte mit überlangem, beweglichem Hals. Das Tier, so die Zeugen, habe unter Zischlauten den Hals in alle Richtungen gedreht und sei langsam wieder in den Fluten des Sees versunken, dabei einen Strudel hinterlassend.

Unter den Zeugen sind auch der katholische Priester des Ortes M. und ein siebenjähriger Junge, der nach seinem Erlebnis unter Schock steht.

Ein auf die Fauna des Sees spezialisierter Biologe der Universität K. sprach in einer ersten Erklärung von den stark differierenden Wassertemperaturen zwischen dem Ost- und dem viel tieferen Westteil des Sees. An der betreffenden Engstelle käme es zu wasserspiegelnahen Nebelbänken, die tatsächliche Erscheinungen extrem verzerren, aber auch vergrößern könnten. Das vermeintliche Ungeheuer sei vermutlich eine Art Nebel-Hologramm eines in der Nähe fischenden Haubentauchers gewesen.

Der Zoologe fügte hinzu, man habe in den vergangenen Jahren wohl einige neue Spezies am M.-See entdeckt, aber alle gehörten dem Süßwasserplankton an und keine von ihnen sei größer als ein halber Millimeter.

II. Aussage Zeuge a (Schüler, 7 Jahre)

ZEUGE 1: Ich hab zuerst gedacht, ein Boot. Oder ein Paragleiter, der auf dem Wasser in der Nähe landet. Das Geräusch ist ja von drüben gekommen, von der Seite, wo die Leute sind. Ich komme an einer Stelle zum See, wo sonst niemand ist. Ich geh immer denselben Weg. Gerade hinunter. Oben ist das Jagdhaus mit dem Hirschgeweih, sie sagen jetzt Verwaltungszentrum dazu. Davor ist ein Parkplatz für die Holzlaster, dann kommt eine Hecke und hinter der Hecke beginnen der Wald und dieser Weg. Er geht immer gerade den Berg hinunter und ganz unten kommen ein paar Felsen, dann der See. Man sieht die Felsen von hier. Schauen Sie. Ein Hohlweg für die Holzarbeiter. Früher haben sie ihn benützt. Das haben sie mir gesagt. Sie haben die Bäume pfeilgerade zum Wasser gezogen und dann über den See schwimmen lassen. Drüben, wo die Leute sind, haben sie zwei Dörfer gebaut. Jetzt haben sie den Parkplatz und die Laster. Am Weg ist lauter fauliges Laub. Riechen Sie es. Es stinkt immer ein bisschen. Ich will ja nicht baden. Ich will am Wasser sein.

III. Recherchen des Chronisten

Der See wurde mit einem kurzbeinigen Hund verglichen, was seine Form angeht. Sehr alte Chroniken kennen das sieben Kilometer lange Gewässer noch als Hundswasser, ehe es 1345 mit der Gründung der Ortschaft M. den Namen M.- See erhielt.

Der Kopf des Hundes schaut nach Westen und stellt den tieferen, paradoxerweise zugleich wärmeren Teil des M.-Sees dar; verantwortlich dafür ist eine siebzig Meter unter der Wasseroberfläche gelegene Quellmündung, durch die Thermalwasser in den See gelangt. Dieser Zufluss und der Schottbach, der in die Schnauzenspitze des Hundes fließt, speisen den See. Der Hundskopf ist der einsame Abschnitt des Sees. Bis auf ein paar kaum genutze Bootsschuppen der Fischer und einer Holzlagerstätte ist er von jenem aus Bergahornen und alten Tannen bestehenden Wald umgeben, den die Bundesforste vor bald einem Jahrzehnt an eine deutsche Holzproduktionsgesellschaft verkauft haben, die das Holz der Bergahorne unter anderem im Instrumentenbau einsetzt.

Die beiden Siedlungen am See, das kleinere M. und das ausgedehnte, erst im Zuge des Sommertourismus auf seine heutige Größe angewachsene U., liegen hingegen am östlichen, seichten Becken des M.-Sees, seit der vorvergangenen Jahrhundertwende hat sich Sommertourismus entwickelt, zu Ostern findet in der Kirche von U. darüber hinaus ein sakrales Musikfest statt. Es gibt drei Segel- und Surfschulen, ein bisschen Landwirtschaft, vor allem Milchviehherden, im flachen Becken östlich des Sees. Südlich des M.-Sees wirft sich sich die Landschaft rasch zu den Höhen des Grenzkogel-Massivs auf, hier weiden die Rinder im Sommer. Die Marktgemeinde M. hat 800 Einwohner, der Straßendorfflecken U. 2.400.

Die Stelle der angeblichen Erscheinung ist die Engstelle zwischen den beiden Seebecken, es herrschen hier Tiefenströmungen in beide Richtungen, der an seiner breitesten Stelle 1,2 Kilometer weite See verengt sich hier zu einem Nadelöhr von nur 40 Meter Breite.

IV. Aussage Zeuge b (Priester, 53 Jahre)

CHRONIST: Und, waren es wirklich sieben Meter? Hochwürden, waren es sieben?

ZEUGE B: Es zählt nicht die Größe dessen, was man sieht. Es zählen die Farbigkeit, finde ich, und die Dichte. Dessen, was man sieht. Ich habe ja einiges gesehen, ich habe Offenbarungen gehabt, Mysterien und Wunder bezeugt, in den Jahren, bevor sie mich hierher geschickt haben. Ich glaube, am meisten habe ich in meinen Probejahren gesehen, im Wienerwald. In diesen Jahren ist man in der Umarmung Gottes. Man halluziniert ununterbrochen. Oder man sieht wirklich mehr als vorher und nachher zusammen. Die Brüder vom Heiligen Kreuz. Bei ihnen war Frater Angelus, der die höheren Weihen nicht hatte, er war der Zimmermann des Stiftes. Früher war er in Fatima, dort hat er mehrere Engel und die heilige Elisabeth gewahrt. Seitdem hat er alles sehen können, die Schutzengel und die kleinen giftigen Dämonen neben dem Weg. Es war sehr lehrreich, mit ihm durch die Landschaft zu gehen. Er hat mich gebeten, ein Evangelium mitzunehmen und es ihm vorzulesen.

Er lese selber nicht so gut, hat er gesagt. Er habe Bergpredigt gelesen, den unreinen Geist in der Schweineherde, die Geschichte vom verlorenen Sohn, immer wieder, das war Frater Angelus Lieblingsgeschichte. Aber in den Pausen hat er mir berichtet, was er alles sieht, am Wegesrand, in den Bäumen, in den Straßenschluchten der Stadt. Auf unseren Rückwegen zum Kloster hab ich die Dinge auch gesehen. Gottes geistige Mitstreiter um das Gute und das Sträuben seiner Widersacher, die gewiss zerquetscht werden würden …

Angelus selbst hat im Wienerwald später mehrfach die Muttergottes gesehen, und wo er sie gesehen hat, hat er Kapellen und Schreine aufstellen lassen, glauben Sie nicht, er hätte da keine Durchsetzungskraft gehabt …

Pause. – Verzeihen Sie. Deswegen sind Sie nicht gekommen.

V. Aussage Zeuge c (Wirt, 40 Jahre)

Mein Partner hat gerudert. Ich habe die Angeln vorbereitet. Man hat uns gesagt, in der Strömung jagen Hechte. Wir haben ja keine Ahnung gehabt.

Er sagt auf einmal: Heast, wir rutschen runter. Und das war wirklich so. Der Seespiegel war plötzlich geneigt, wir sind runtergerutscht, Richtung Westen, auf die Engstelle und den Waldkessel, den Hundskopf zu. Nicht schnell, aber so, dass man es merkt. Und wie wir hinübergeschaut haben, haben wir gesehen, dass es auf der anderen Seite, im Waldkessel, wieder raufgeht, das muss man sich vorstellen, ein Wasser, das runter- und wieder raufgeht. Der Moses fällt einem ein und das Volk Israel und das Meer, das auseinander geht.

Eine Verwerfung. Das Boot ist ganz sacht abwärts getrieben, mein Partner war schneeweiß im Gesicht, dann haben wir die anderen gespürt. Wir standen plötzlich in Verbindung mit ihnen. Mit dem Pfarrer, mit der Frau in ihrem Bootshaus und dem kleinen Buben im Wald auf der anderen Seite. Wir wussten, dass sie da waren und sie spürten uns auch. Was da passiert, hat uns zu einer einzigen Wahrnehmung gemacht. Wir wären beinahe untergetaucht. Das ist die Wahrheit. Es hat dann jede Menge Gischt oder Nebel gegeben. Und es ist ... es ist direkt vor uns ganz aufgegangen. Das Wasser. Schauen Sie einmal zur Engstelle. Auf der anderen Seite ist da ein kleines felsiges Kap.

Ungefähr dort war unser Boot, als das passiert ist, das Wasser war bei uns wieder flach, alles war bewegungslos, aber nicht einmal zehn Meter vor uns ist es steil hinuntergegangen. Wohin? Wir haben es nicht gesehen. Wir waren zu nahe am Wasser. Wir haben nur den Eingang des Schlauches gesehen.

VI. Recherchen des Chronisten

In den Wäldern leben Rot- und Rehwild, Füchse, Dachse und Marder kommen vor, vereinzelt, so das Forstamt, wandern im Herbst die Bären durch. Seltene Rabenvögel wie Alpenkrähe und Alpendohle, aber auch Steinadler leben im Massiv des S.-Kogels, außerdem nisten in Tannen Eichelhäher, Steinkauz und Schleiereule. In den Feuchtgebieten am Ostende des Sees leben Gras- und Moorfrosch, Ringel- und Würfelnatter, auf Sonnenlagen des S.-Kogels und in Kahlschlägen des Ahornwaldes kommt die schwarze Unterart der Kreuzotter, die Höllenotter, vor. Auf den Wiesen im Süden und Osten des Sees sollen im Sommer zahlreiche, schon südlichere Schmetterlingsarten zu beobachten sein. Der See ist Heimat für Welse, Schuppenkarpfen, Saiblinge, Hechte und Barsche und Kleinfische, Berg- und Kammmolche; in einem seiner Zuflüsse, dem Schottbach, gibt es Edelkrebse.

Niemals hat jemand hier ein Tier gesehen, das größer gewesen wäre als eine Kuh.

Auch die Zeugen, mit denen ich jetzt gesprochen habe, schildern zwar absolut außergewöhnliche Wahrnehmungen wie Löcher oder rasche Veränderungen des Seeniveaus, von einem schildkrötenartigen Wesen ist aber niemals die Rede.

Nach dem Vorfall wurden einige der Zeugen ärztlich behandelt. Der örtliche Polizeipostenkommandant machte eine Meldung, die von der Pressestelle der Landesregierung in elektronischer Form an die Agenturen weitergegeben wurde. Erst in diesem Text ist erstmals von einem «Tier» die Rede. Die populärwissenschaftliche Agentur *interfakt* und daraufhin die *Frankfurter* haben die Meldung übernommen, ein Monster gesäugt, das, wie es scheint, die Landespolitiker geboren haben.

Allerdings ist hier, wie ich glaube, abgesehen von solchen Behauptungen, tatsächlich etwas Erstaunliches geschehen.

VII. Aussage Zeuge a (Schüler)

An dem Tag bin ich ganz schnell hinuntergekommen, ich bin gelaufen, weil ich hab was bauen wollen. Es war zeitig in der Früh. Ich hab oben beim Forsthaus nicht gewartet, bis mir das Kindermädchen ein Frühstück bringt. Ich bin gleich los. Ich wollte ein Baumhaus bauen, hab sogar Nägel mitgebracht und einen Hammer. Meine Mami ist ja vier Tage später gekommen, ich wollt's bis dahin fertig haben. Den Baum hab ich schon ausgesucht, ein paar Äste gehen über das Wasser hinaus, gleich sind wir unten, dann sehen wir ihn. Aber wie ich unten war, hab ich erst gemerkt, was ich nicht bedacht hab. Dass die Hölzer, die ich auf den Baum hab nageln wollen, zu schwer waren. Außerdem waren sie zu lang. Säge hab ich keine mitgehabt. Wo krieg ich eine her, hab ich noch gedacht. Die Holzarbeiter trauen sich sicher nicht, mir eine zu borgen, weil dann das Kindermädchen schreit.

Ich hab grad überlegt, wo sie ihre Sägen aufbewahren, dann war das Geräusch da.

Ein Geräusch, wie wenn man Apfelsaft mit dem Strohhalm trinkt, und Luft geht mit. So ein Geräusch, aber in groß. Als Nächstes hab ich schon gesehen, dass ein Loch im See ist, ein großes Loch, größer als die meisten Boote, genau da, wo der See eng wird. Das Geräusch ist lauter geworden, ich war direkt am Wasser, aber dann bin ich hinaufgelaufen, zurück, bis hierher, wo wir jetzt stehen. Das Geräusch, das Saugen ist noch stärker geworden, und plötzlich war es ganz weg. Alles war leise. Da hab ich mich noch einmal umgedreht. Und da war das Loch fertig, wie ein Schlauch, der immer in eine andere Richtung in den See hineingegangen ist, als würde er unter Wasser herumschwingen.

VIII. Aussage Zeuge B (Priester)

Unser Ungeheuer zieht sich niemals zurück, es ist kein Reptil und auch sonst kein Tier, das man mit den Augen sieht. Im Namen des Vater, des Sohens und des Heiligen Geistes. Wir sind da.

Die einzige Statue des heiligen Koloman südlich der Alpen. Die meisten stehen im Waldviertel und schauen Richtung Donautal, man weiß nicht genau, warum das so ist. Aber die Figur dieses Bildstocks steht hier im Süden und schaut nach Triest. Zu Beginn des siebzehnten Jahrhunderts erbaut, wohl von einem fahrenden Mönch mit Heimweh. Das würde ich gut verstehen. Ich fahre nicht gern auf dem Wasser. Ich glaube, nicht einmal der Herrgott ist gern drauf spazieren gegangen. Und hab ich nicht Recht gehabt? Ist nicht gerade im Wasser die Tür zum großen Verneiner aufgegangen? Dieses Loch ...

CHRONIST: Weshalb, glauben Sie, macht die Landesregierung einen zischenden Schildkrötendrachen aus eurem Loch?

PRIESTER: Ja, verstehen Sie das nicht? Sie wohnen in der Villa Monteverdi. Haben Sie die Herren der Landesregierung nicht gesehen, wenn sie mit ihren Hofschranzen essen und saufen kommen? Sie sündigen mit ihren Huren, ihren Brüdern und Schwestern, ihren Müttern und ihren Hunden. Dabei berufen sie sich auf das Echte und auf die Natur. Sie wollen ja das Land vom Rest des Staates trennen. Sie wollen Raubritter spielen und nachher im See baden. Sie sind alle verrückt und sie sind böse.

Die Landesregierung braucht genau so etwas, ein Tier, das aus einem Zaubersee wie unserem sein schmutziges Haupt erhebt, ein Monster, ein Schutzgespenst, einen Dämon für ihre Köpfe und ihr kommendes Wappen. Diese Lausbuben werden einen Wallfahrtsort für Ungeheuerfreunde erbauen, einen Heidenbrauch begründen, der wie eine Feuerwalze über meine Kirche kommen wird.

IX. Aussage Zeuge a (Schüler)

Der Schlauch ist durchgegangen. Durch alles. Den See, die Erde, durch den Ozean auf der anderen Seite der Erde, hinaus in den Weltraum. An der Innenseite von dem Schlauch sind wie im Kino auf der großen Wand Gesichter gewesen, die haben gezittert, die Gesichter der Frau und der Männer im Boot, das vom Pfarrer, sogar Ihr Gesicht.

Komisch, oder; wir haben uns noch gar nicht gekannt. Ihr Gesicht war mir nicht fremd. Es ist da keine Zeit mehr vergangen. Außerdem war es kalt und ich ...

Stimme versinkt im Sturm.

CHRONIST: Bitte?

Ende.

Seite 356

Stimmen aus dem Jenseits

---   —

von Andreas Schett

---   —

Der Witwe Rosemary Brown erschienen ab 1964 in ihrem Haus in einem Vorort von London alle große Komponisten der Musikgeschichte. Bach, Schubert, Liszt (und wie sie alle heißen, die Meister der Tonschöpfung) diktierten der Hausfrau brandneue, nach ihrem Ableben entstandene Stücke. Als Rosemary vor vier Jahren starb, hinterließ sie mehr als 400 Kompositionen, zwei Schallplatten und das Buch: «Musik aus dem Jenseits», das Andreas Schett mehrmals quergelesen hat.

```
«Absender: +4369910137788 Gesendet: 09:42:34 26.02.2004
Das Medium spricht —»
«Absender: +4369919436917 Gesendet: 09:43:56 26.02.2004
Da wird mir ganz flauschig um mein Herz.»
```

Beginnen wir mit dem Klappentext:

Im Jenseits gibt es Berge, Flüsse, Wälder und viele schöne Blumen und die Menschen sehen dort viel jünger, schöner und gesünder aus. Sie lernen Sprachen, malen Bilder, komponieren ...
Diese und viele andere Informationen – sie stammen von Liszt, Schubert, Beethoven und Bach, von insgesamt 12 ganz berühmten Musikern, die Rosemary Brown ihre neuesten, im Jenseits entstandenen Werke diktieren.
Über 400 Musikstücke schrieb das Medium, zum Teil vor Fernsehkameras, in kürzester Zeit nieder. Wissenschaftler, Komponisten von Rang und Psychologen erklären: Rosemary Browns Musik aus dem Jenseits ist – verblüffenderweise – echt.

«Ich bin ganz einfach der Empfänger.»

«Ich nehme auf, was gerade kommt.»

«An Mrs. Browns medialer Begabung ist nicht zu zweifeln.» (Der Spiegel)

Und jetzt auf der Stelle eine gute Geschichte:

Im Jahre 1969 erkundigten sich die Leute vom Dritten Programm der BBC bei mir, ob ich bereit sei, bei einer Dokumentarsendung über meine Arbeit mitzuwirken. Ehrlich gesagt, ich hatte einige Zweifel. Als ich dieses Angebot erhielt, fragte ich Liszt, was er davon halte. Er hatte überhaupt keine Zweifel. «Das musst du machen», sagte er. Die Sendung bestand teilweise aus einer hochnotpeinlichen Befragung, wie wir sie alle gut kennen. Dann fragte man mich etwas, das ich schon oft gefragt wurde: Ob ich bereit oder imstande sei, während der Sendung mit einem Komponisten in Verbindung zu treten. «Ich will es versuchen», sagte ich, «aber ich kann nichts garantieren.» Die Leute von der BBC waren einverstanden. Wir versammelten uns in dem Zimmer, in dem ich arbeite. Ich brachte Tee und wartete, ob etwas geschehen würde. Schon nach wenigen Minuten erschien Liszt, verlässlich wie immer. Er sah sehr ruhig und gefasst aus und sagte, er wolle versuchen, mir ein neues Musikstück zu übermitteln. «Wenn möglich etwas ganz Besonderes», sagte ich zu ihm, und er lächelte wissend. Zuerst gab er mir den Notenschlüssel. «Es sind sechs Kreuz», sagte er, «der Takt ist 5/4 für die rechte Hand und 3/2 für die linke.» Das war sehr schwer. Verärgert wandte ich mich um und sah, dass er selbstzufrieden lächelte. Bis dahin hatte er mir noch nie so schwierige Musik übermittelt. «Versuch nur», meinte Liszt beruhigend, «mach schon.» Die Noten waren für mich viel zu schwierig, als dass ich vom Blatt hätte spielen können. Ich konnte einfach nicht gleichzeitig im 5/4 und im 3/2 Takt spielen und kam immer mehr durcheinander. Dann fragte der Redakteur, ob ich was dagegen hätte, wenn er es einmal versuchte. Ich hatte bis dahin nicht gewusst, dass er ein guter Pianist war. Es klang sehr interessant, und als er geendet hatte, herrschte völlige Stille. Dann wandte er sich ganz langsam um und sagte: «Mrs. Brown, ich glaube, da ist wirklich was dran.» Da fiel mir ein Stein vom Herzen!

Liszt, ja freilich. Zum ersten Mal erschien er Rosemary Brown, als jene noch ein Kind war. Rosy war gerade munter geworden, als ein Mann in schwarzer Soutane und mit langem, weißem Haupthaar vor ihrem Bettchen stand. «Wenn du erwachsen bist, werde ich wiederkommen und dir Musik bringen», sagte er.

Das dauerte ein bisschen: Rosemary Browns Mann war bereits einer Leberzirrhose erlegen, sie hatte allein für ihre zwei Kinder im Alter von acht und viereinhalb zu sorgen und nahm eine Stelle als Küchenhilfe an, Anfang der 60er Jahre, London, große Not. Da kam Liszt: «Wahrscheinlich musste (er) den richtigen Zeitpunkt abwarten.» Anfänglich war die stille Gegenwart des weißhaarigen Mannes einfach nur «ein großer Trost»; von Musik keine Rede. Als Rosemary einmal nicht wusste, mit welchem Geld sie Geschenke für ihre Kinder kaufen sollte, riet ihr Liszt: Vielleicht solltest du Fußballtoto spielen. Sie gewann, einmal 10 und ein andermal 51 Pfund. Ob Mrs. Brown die richtigen

Zahlen hellsehen kann? (So etwas Praktisches!) – Die Antwort ist einfach: «Ich kann es nicht und ich werde es niemals können.»

Jedenfalls ereignet sich in genau dieser Zeit: die Erweckung –

Ich hatte einen Unfall. Ich glaube, dass ich zwei gebrochene Rippen hatte, da aber im Krankenhaus keine Röntgenaufnahmen gemacht wurden, werde ich es wohl nie wissen. Ich war eine Woche lang im Krankenstand und sollte möglichst nichts tun. Ich las und strickte ein wenig und eines Tages kam ich auf den Gedanken, mir die Zeit am Klavier zu vertreiben. An diesem Nachmittag erschien mir Liszt. Ich sah ihn ganz klar und deutlich neben mir stehen. Anstatt nun ein Musikstück auszuwählen und es zu spielen, fühlte ich plötzlich, wie er meine Hände auf dem Klavier lenkte. Die Musik erklang, ohne dass ich etwas dazu getan hätte, und es war eine Musik, die ich noch nie zuvor gehört hatte. Heute ist Liszt der Organisator und Führer einer Gruppe berühmter Komponisten, die mich in meinem Heim besuchen und mir ihre neuesten Kompositionen geben.

Die vielen Noten, das ist nicht alles: Liszt löscht Zimmerbrände und macht Rosemary beim Einkaufen auf Sonderangebote aufmerksam und:

So seltsam es klingen mag: Ich glaube mit Recht sagen zu können, dass Liszt mir ein guter Freund geworden ist. Wir plaudern über alle möglichen Dinge miteinander, über ernste Dinge, wie den Sinn des Lebens und Metaphysisches.

Er ist ein sehr schöner Mann mit wunderbaren Umgangsformen. Er ist elegant und würdevoll und ein große Romantiker. Er sagt so nette Dinge, dass man dabei unwillkürlich denkt: «Das ist noch ein echter Kavalier.»

Wie sehr Liszt an meinem Familienleben teilnimmt, möchte ich an einem anderen Beispiel zeigen: Wie er einmal meinem Sohn Thomas bei den Hausarbeiten geholfen hat. Eines Abends war Thomas eben dabei, seine Mathematikaufgabe zu machen, und er fragte mich: «Mammy, wie viel ist eins zum Quadrat plus zwei zum Quadrat plus drei zum Quadrat plus vier zum Quadrat plus ...» Er hatte den Satz noch nicht beendet, da sagte Liszt, der bei mir war, schon: «Dreihundertfünfundachtzig.»

Außerdem spricht Liszt mittlerweile ein fehlerloses Englisch. Immerhin etwas, was man von Bach nicht behaupten kann:

Bach ist streng. Eigentlich arbeite ich nicht besonders gerne mit ihm zusammen. Er scheint keinen Sinn für Humor zu haben. Ich habe ihn noch kein einziges Mal lächeln gesehen und er gibt sich immer sehr distanziert, aber vielleicht nur mir gegenüber. Wenn er ins Haus kommt, dann gibt es nur Arbeit, Arbeit und nochmals Arbeit. Ich bewundre und respektiere ihn sehr, doch konnte ich ihm nie sehr nahe kommen. Er spricht ein wenig Englisch, was er sich vermutlich drüben selbst beigebracht hat, denn ich glaube nicht, dass er zu Lebzeiten Englisch konnte. Ich würde ihn gerne danach fragen, aber ich wage es nicht! Ich habe nur seine Musik entgegenzunehmen, und damit basta.

Moment, das ist ungerecht. Warum gerade SIE?

Die Antwort auf die Frage «Warum gerade Sie?» ist etwas verwickelter, aber Liszt hat mir das erklärt. Ich legte ihm dieselbe Frage vor – «Warum gerade ich?» – und er sagte: «Weil du dafür bereit warst, und zwar schon lange, ehe du geboren wurdest.»

Na also. An der musikalischen Befähigung konnte es nicht liegen. Man wirft mir vor, ich hätte eine fundierte musikalische Ausbildung genossen, klagt Rosemary, aber Schnecke. Als Kind ein Jahr lang üben auf einem verstimmten Klavier in einem unbeheizten Salon des elterlichen Hauses; in Mädchenjahren zwei Semester lang währender, selbst finanzierter Unterricht bei einer Absolventin der Royal Academy; dann der Krieg; schließlich noch einmal, 1951-52, kurz vor der Heirat: Klavierstunden.

Wenn man mich schon als Mittlerin auserkoren und für diese Aufgabe vorgesehen hat, fragte ich Liszt, warum hat man mich dann nicht in einer Familie auf die Welt kommen lassen, in der ich eine bessere Musikerziehung bekommen hätte? «Du hast für unsere Zwecke genügend Ausbildung», sagte er. «Wenn du eine wirklich umfassende Ausbildung erhalten hättest, dann würde uns dies überhaupt nichts nützen. Eine umfassende Musikausbildung hätte es dir erstens noch schwerer gemacht zu beweisen, dass du unsere Musik nicht selbst komponieren konntest. Zweitens hättest du auf Grund eines gründlichen Musikverständnisses eigene Gedanken und Theorien entwickeln können, und die wären wiederum uns hinderlich gewesen.»

Rosemary hatte wie gesagt keinen Tau –

Oft denke ich, man sollte sich doch einmal die Zeit nehmen und richtig zuhören, aber wenn es sich nicht um ein sehr kurzes und interessantes Musikstück handelt, wird es mir bald langweilig und ich werde nervös. Ich bin leider ein viel zu aktiver Mensch, als dass ich ruhig sitzen und zuhören könnte. Jedenfalls kann ich überhaupt nicht unterscheiden, von wem nun welche Musik stammt. Manchmal drehe ich das Radio an und sage zu meine Tochter: «Das ist Schubert! Nein, es ist Mozart. Oder kann es Beethoven sein?» Ich irre mich fast immer.

Auftritt, Schubert:

Ich finde Schubert liebenswert. Ich glaube, jeder würde ihn mögen.

Wenn ich mich recht erinnere, trug er beim ersten Mal Brillen. Ich glaube, das tat er nur, damit ich ihn leichter erkennen könne, denn im Jenseits benötigt er ja keine Brillen und seither trägt er sie auch nicht mehr, wenn er mich besucht. Ich bemerkte, dass Schubert ein wirklich schöner Mann war, vor allem, weil er nicht so feist und dickwangig aussieht wie auf den meisten Abbildungen. Er ist äußerst bescheiden und unauffällig, auf seine Art sehr still und fröhlich, aber sein Humor ist etwas altmodisch.

Übrigens, wenn wir an seinen Liedern arbeiten, versucht er manchmal, sie mir vorzusingen. Leider hat er keine sehr gute Stimme. Ich habe mir vorgestellt, dass man nach der Ankunft im Jenseits sofort eine gute Singstimme erhält – doch dies widerspricht meiner Annahme.

Ich habe sogar das Ende der Unvollendeten Symphonie gehört, das ganz besonders schön ist. Schubert ließ es mich durch Telepathie hören. Einige Komponisten können das und sie vermögen auch die Zeit so zu «komprimieren», dass ich tatsächlich eine ganzes Konzert oder eine Symphonie in wenigen Minuten hören kann. Ich hoffe, einmal für Schubert den letzten Satz seiner Unvollendeten niederschreiben zu können – aber ich glaube, dass das eine lange und schwere Aufgabe sein wird.

Wenn Schubert mir ein Musikstück gibt, sagt er am Schluss meist sehr besorgt: «Hat es dir gefallen?», als wäre er ein wenig unsicher und brauchte Bestätigung. Jedenfalls ist er da seiner Sache nicht sehr sicher.

Schubert trägt keine Brillen mehr und Beethoven ist übrigens nicht mehr taub!

Beethoven war mir lange Zeit ein Rätsel. Natürlich ist er nicht mehr taub. Solche menschlichen Leiden und Gebrechen verschwinden im Jenseits. Manchmal spricht er über Musik, manchmal über sich selbst, über das Leben oder über Gott. Eines Tages sprach er so ruhig und gütig mit mir, dass ich, zutiefst gerührt und demütig, zu ihm sagte: «Beethoven – ich liebe dich!» Er sah mich mit dem Anflug eines Lächelns an und sagte dann ganz ernst: «Natürlich.»

Derselbe Beethoven war es auch, der die Nerven verlor. «Beethoven ließ keinen Zweifel, dass er die Übermittlung seiner Musik als Zeitverschwendung betrachten würde, wenn man keine Anstalten machte, sie zu verbreiten.» Also kam irgendwann die BBC. Wie es so weit kam?

Mrs. Browns Mutter lag am Totenbett. «Versprich mir eines», sagte sie zu ihrer Tochter, «geh' nach meinem Tod zu Mrs. Hosgood», versprich mir, «dass du zu ihr gehst.» Rosemary versprach's und nur wenige Tage nach der Beerdigung der Mutter stand die leibhaftige Mrs. Hosgood, eine mit einem Rettungsdienstbeamten verheiratete Hellseherin, direkt vor der Haustür. «Ihre Mutter hat mich geschickt!», sagte sie. Rosemary ging zu den spiritistischen Sitzungen der Mrs. Hosgood, dort wiederum gab es eine gewisse Mrs. Pendleton, die während des Gottesdienstes der Spiritistenkirche die Orgel spielte und einen Ersatz für den Fall suchte, dass sie nicht konnte. Rosemary konnte nicht Nein sagen, aber machte, während die Gemeinde sang, die schrecklichsten Fehler. Also schlich sie sich oft heimlich in die Kirche, um zu üben. Irgendwann beschloss sie aufzuhören. «Ich bitte dich dringend, damit fortzufahren», sagte Liszt. «Es ist von größter Wichtigkeit!»

Wieder üben. Einmal an einem Samstagnachmittag: Eine Mrs. Glady Smith hält zur selben Zeit eine okkulte Beratungsstunde ab und es kommt nur eine Besucherin, da der berühmte Heilpraktiker Mr. Edwards in der Stadt weilt. Mrs. Glady Smith bleibt nichts anderes übrig, als zu warten, ob nicht doch noch jemand erscheint. Dabei hört sie Rosemarys Orgelspiel (Liszt hat bereits mit der Vermittlung von Musik begonnen.)

«Spielen Sie weiter!» Und: «Von wem ist das?»
«Die Musik ist sozusagen geistig inspiriert worden.»
«Wissen Sie nicht, wer sie inspirierte? War es eine bestimmte Person?»
«Ich glaube, es könnte Liszt sein.»

Mrs. Smith kennt Leute in Wimbledon, eine Vereinigung für okkulte und spiritistische Forschung, darunter Hilary Wontner und dessen Frau Judith, die wiederum in irgendeiner Weise mit Betty Francis und deren Gatten Karl bekannt sind, weshalb auch ein Kontakt zu Mary Rogers erfolgt und es eines Tages zu einer Begegnung mit Sir George Trevelyan kommt, der seinerseits die von Rosemary aufgepinselten Noten einer Mrs. Mary Firth zeigt, zu der sich ein gewisser Major MacManaway dazu gesellt, woraufhin die drei letztgenannten eine Stiftung gründen, auf dass Rosemary mehr Zeit für die Musik habe, als eines Tages Monica Sims von der BBC am Telefonapparat ist, worüber Sir George und Mrs. Firth fürchterlich entsetzt sind ... nun, Rosemary tut es trotzdem. Im Interesse der Komponisten aus dem Jenseits –

Aber jetzt wieder zur Arbeit:

Ich glaube, es warten noch andere, sozusagen «hinter den Kulissen», um sich der Gruppe anzuschließen und ihre Musik zu übermitteln. Sie sind mir selbstverständlich alle will-

kommen. Mein einziges Problem ist, genügend Zeit zu finden, um all die Arbeit zu tun, die sie für mich planen.

Wir haben eine Arbeitsweise entwickelt, an die ich mich zu halten bemühe. Ich schicke die Kinder zur Schule, mache meine Hausarbeit und arbeite dann von etwa zehn bis dreizehn Uhr an der Musik. Der Komponist, der an diesem Tag mit mir arbeitet, verlässt mich dann, damit ich Mittagessen kann, und erscheint wiederum gegen halb zwei. Dann arbeiten wir bis etwa halb fünf. Dann muss ich aufhören, um das Essen für die Kinder zu bereiten. An den Abenden wird jedoch wieder gearbeitet, auch an den Wochenenden.

Wenn man so vieles an einem einzigen Tag unterzubringen hat, ist es eine einzige Plage mit einem wie Debussy:

Debussy gehört nicht zu meinen regelmäßigen Besuchern. Er ist manchmal ein wenig unstet. Manchmal kommt er jeden Tag und dann sehe ich ihn lange Zeit überhaupt nicht. Ich hatte von ihm bereits eine Anzahl Klavierwerke erhalten und er hatte mit der Arbeit an einem Septett begonnen, war jedoch noch nicht sehr weit damit gekommen. Ich glaube, es wird sehr interessant werden, aber meinem Sohn Thomas gefällt es nicht. Jedes Mal, wenn ich die Themen auf dem Klavier spiele, verkriecht er sich, weil ihm diese Musik sehr disharmonisch vorkommt.

Ich glaube, dass Debussy in gewissem Sinne ein Opfer der Konventionen seiner Zeit war. Heute leben Tausende von Menschen so, wie er damals lebte, sie tragen seltsame Kleidung und schlafen manchmal mit Frauen, die nicht ihre Gattinnen sind. Heute kümmert sich niemand viel darum, aber damals war das anders.

Das Interessanteste an Debussy ist vielleicht, dass er im Jenseits zu malen begonnen hat. Er hat auch zwei Bilder gemalt, die er «Sonnenaufgang» und «Sonnenuntergang» nannte. Sie sind natürlich in den Farben des Sonnenlichts gehalten, überwiegend in Rot und Orange. Die Bilder sind wunderschön und es ist wirklich schade, dass die Welt sie nicht sehen kann. Ich finde Debussy sehr amüsant. Er wird gewöhnlich mit einem Bart dargestellt, jetzt aber ist er glatt rasiert.

Und zum Schluss das Beste – es ist wahr:

Ich habe schon früher auf die verschiedenen Theorien hingewiesen, die man ersinnt, um meine Musik wegzuerklären. Eine davon besagt, dass ich an Kryptomnesie, verborgenen Erinnerungen «leide». Eine andere deutet an, dass mit meinem Geisteszustand etwas nicht in Ordnung sei. Nun, beides ist unrichtig, und ich darf mit Befriedigung feststellen, dass einer der größten Experten der Welt auf dem Gebiet der Parapsychologie umfangreiche Tests mit mir gemacht hat, und dass die Ergebnisse dieser Tests beide Theorien wider-

legen. Der Parapsychologe ist Professor Tenhaeff. Als Philips die erste Langspielplatte mit Musik der Komponisten auf den Markt brachte, fragte man mich, ob ich bereit wäre, mich von Professor Tenhaeff und seinem Team gründlich testen zu lassen. In einer Erklärung für die Weltpresse stellte er fest: «Das Ergebnis zeigte, dass wir es mit einer geistig gesunden Frau zu tun haben, die keinen Wert darauf legt, im Mittelpunkt des Interesses zu stehen. Eher ist das Gegenteil der Fall. Mein Mitarbeiter, ein Anstalts-psychiater mit langjähriger Erfahrung, konnte keinerlei geistige Anormalität feststellen. Auch unsere psychodiagnostische Untersuchung ergab nicht den geringsten Anhaltspunkt für eine geistige Fehlentwicklung. Weitere Untersuchungen sind geplant, an denen sich auch bekannte Musikfachleute beteiligen werden. Unter den zahllosen Fällen, die mir im Verlaufe vieler Jahre zur Kenntnis gelangt sind, ist der Fall Rosemary Brown sicherlich einer der interessantesten. Sie ist außerdem einer der sympathischsten und nicht zuletzt einer der vernünftigsten Menschen.» Trotz der vielen Schwierigkeiten, denen ich mich gegenübersehe, bin ich sehr glücklich, dass die Musik aus dem Jenseits endlich Anerkennung findet. Und ich hoffe, dass die Welt eines Tages diese Musik als echtes Geschenk aus dem Jenseits anerkennen wird, und dass damit die Arbeit der Komponisten nicht vergebens war.

Wir wollen Rosemary Brown ebenso viel Glauben schenken wie Nikolaus Harnoncourt –

Credits

\---   -

+rosebud no.5 – Mystery

\---   -

PUBLISHER
Ralf Herms

CONCEPT DESIGNER
Fritz T. Magistris

EDITORS IN CHIEF
Ralf Herms
Katja Fössel
Fritz T. Magistris

ART DIRECTORS
Katja Fössel
Ralf Herms

CONTRIBUTING EDITORS
Wolfgang Gosch
Erich Pöttschacher

TRANSLATIONS
Douglas Merril
Lidia Nonato
Astrid Tautscher

PROOFREADING
Hubert Kapaun
Douglas Merril

IMAGE PROCESSING
Mario Rott

PAPER
Curtis by Curtis 1.0, 135 g/m^2,
available through
Römerturm Feinstpapier
www.roemerturm.com

PRINTING & BINDING
Jütte-Messedruck
Ostwaldstraße 4
D-04329 Leipzig/Germany
www.juette-messedruck.de

EDITORIAL OFFICES
Rosebud, Inc./Germany
Pelzetleite 65
D-90614 Ammerndorf
T. +49 (0)1 72 / 894 22 90

Rosebud, Inc./Austria
Heinrichsgasse 2/1/8
A-1010 Vienna
T. +43 (0)6 99 / 19 43 69 17

ask@rosebudmagazine.com
www.rosebudmagazine.com

DISTRIBUTION
Die Gestalten Verlag GmbH
& Co. KG, Berlin (dgv)
Münzstrasse 15
D-10178 Berlin/Germany
www.die-gestalten.de

Respect copyright, encourage creativity! For your local dgv-distributor please check: www.die-gestalten.de

This publication was supported by

Our thanks to all our friends and families—especially: Helga, Hellmuth, Ina, Anke & Ute, Leisha; Alice, Flo, Conny, April; K.; Wolfgang Stögmann, Günter Parth, Nadine Blanchard & Christian Anwander; Gipo, Nina, Yudi, Birgit, Erwin, Claire, Christoph, Peter and Lilly; Frank Stowasser, Claudia Berker, Joachim Gaida, Sabine Mayhofer, Susumo Ono, Abudi Hönig, Julia Barnes and all those who by some means or other supported us in realizing this issue.

The Not-So-Usual Suspects

To shed a little light on the mystery of the contributors of this issue we asked them some questions: Name? Profession? Date of birth? Current residence? Most mysterious thing in life?

1) Chloë Potter · Photographer/Artist · 23.8.73 · Austria & USA · «The human heart.» 2) Peter Schattschneider · Professor of Physics · 7.3.50 · Paris/France · «Life.» 3) Timo Reger · Designer · Jan. '71 · Nuremberg/Germany · «My birth.» 4) Marc Calvary · Photocopy drone by day, Creator & Publisher of «the carbon based mistake» by night. (www.thecarbonbasedmistake.com) · 30.3.75 · Eugene, Oregon/USA · «My wife.» 5) Mathias Kessler · Photographer · 30.5.68 · NYC/USA · «Perception.» 6) Alexander Kellas · Artist · 1.8.70 · NYC/USA · «Life itself, seems very mysterious to me.» 7) Frankie Mayer · Styling Creative Direction · not available · Paris/France 8) Dr. Jerry William Cullum (Photo: www.twmeyer.com) · Art Critic & Curator · 7.6.46 · Atlanta, Georgia/USA · «Long runs of meaningful coincidence.» 9) Christoph Friedrich Wilhelm Brunmayr (www.menonthemoon.com) · Tourist · 6.2.71 · Vienna/Austria · «Consciousness.» 10) Prof. Peter W. Mulacz · Parapsychologist · not available · Vienna/Austria · «Life as such is the greatest mystery of all.» 11) Janusz Daga · Art Director · 10.5.75 · Verona/Italy · «My girlfriend.» 12) Interkool— Sabine Feichtner · 8.3.69 and Christoph Steinegger · 19.11.71 · Communication · Hamburg/Germany · «Every new day.»

13) Anna Gerber · Designer & Writer · 10.6.73 · London/UK · «The baby growing inside me.» 14) Marc Kulicke · Student of Communication Design · 30.9.77 · Würzburg/Germany · «Abandoned Buildings.» 15) Lisa Gayle Marshall · Graphic Designer & Artist · 24.5.71 · Vancouver, BC/Canada · «Wolfgang Gosch.» 16) Alexander Egger · Gestalter · 4.11.71 · Vienna/Europe · «The man in my bathroom mirror staring at me.» 17) Ernst Schmiederer · Journalist & Author · 14.8.59 · Vienna & Unterretzbach/Austria · «Lots of things (for instance the light switch), and mankind as a whole.» 18) Thomas Smetana · to live · 29.5.66 · Zaubertal/Austria · «Women.» 19) They never told me · I don't know · I never asked · In the east · «Other people and that I hurt them.» 20) peach: Birgit Vollmeier · Mother, Lover, Creative Director · 3.11.67, Yudi Warsosumarto · Professional Doubter, Art Director, Graphic Designer · 20.12.69, Irene Grundl · Colour & Shape Inspirator, Graphic Designer · 1.5.82 · Vienna/Austria · «The enormous power of love and will.» 21) Nataliya Slinko · Artist & Designer · 5.9.73 · NYC/USA · «Consistency of waking up every morning.» 22) Tiziana Panizza · Concept Designer · 6.8.59 · Rome & Milan/Italy · «See page 185.» 23) Liana Miuccio · Photographer (www.lianaphoto.com) · 31.11.65 · Rome/Italy & NYC/USA · «Creating photographic images that reflect my past, my present and my future.» 24) Sofie Moons · Graphic Designer & Illustrator · 1.8.75 · Antwerp/Belgium · «Wrapped gifts.» 25) Jeffrey Lin · a visual person · 16.4.77 · Queens, NYC/USA · «My ability to control time while appearing not to do so.» 26) Sergio del Puerto · Graphic Designer & Illustrator · 12.4.78 · Madrid/Spain · «Sleep a siesta for 6 hours!» 27) Mark Glassner · Research engineer · 26.4.72 · London/UK · «Outer space.» 28) Wolfgang Gosch · Surveyor · 9.3.77 · Graz/Austria · «Coincidence. Tastes like magic.» 29) Lorenzo Petrantoni · Art Director · 17.11.70 · Milan/Italy · «My life.» 30) Michael Dürr · Photographer · 8.4.71 · Vienna/Austria · «The Austrian Alps.» 31) Ernst Berthold Otto Friedrich Molden · Author, Singer & Songwriter · 19.11.67 · Vienna/Austria · «My two sons.» 32) Silja Götz · Illustrator · 14.4.74 · Madrid/Spain · «There's many things I don't have an answer for, so there's a lot of mystery.»

33) tonho/Quinta-feira · Graphic Designer · 15.12.77 · Rio de
Janeiro/Brasil · «Next few seconds.» 34) Ella Propella · taking
a close look · Winter · Berlin/Germany · «The future.» 36) Heidi
Hackl · Costume Designer & Communication Designer · 15.3.65 ·
Innsbruck/Austria · «To sleep.» 35) Andreas Schett · Musician, Composer, Communication Designer & Publisher (www.circus.at) ·
4.12.71 · Innsbruck/Austria · «The Queenbee in early summer.»
37) Oliver Tissot · better remains a secret · not verified under mysterious circumstances · unknown · «My Life.» 38) Sandro Baldoni ·
Film Director · 20.12.54 · Rome/Italy · «My mother's smile.» 39)
Jordan Crane · Artist & Designer · Dec. '72 · NYC/USA · «My wife.»
40) freude · Ideas · 2.1.03 · Vienna/Austria · «Lady Di's death.» with
Wolfgang Zajc · Photographer · 27.8.67 · «My new girlfriend.» 41)
Anke Dessin · Artist · 19.5.65 · Berlin/Germany · «I used to go for
long walks with a shoebox and a rope attached to it. It was my
dog called Corso. The shoebox got ripped on the bottom because the grass was high and wet. I still remember calling out for
Corso when he got stuck in the green grass.» 42) Mike Meiré · Art
Director, Designer & Negotiator · '64 · Cologne/Germany · «The
trust in logic.» 43) Silke Stock · Sculptor · 22.7.63 · Karls-
ruhe/Germany · «At the top it has an irregular sphere with several holes that can be used to fill something in. Attached to it is a
cylindric tubing that leads into another container, which is slightly bigger (...)» 44) Daniel Roth · Artist · 26.10.69 · Karlsruhe/
Germany · «Death.» 45) Erich Pöttschacher · Shapeshifter ·
4.8.68 · Vienna/Austria · «Once in a week I feel synchronized
with my radio and television-set. I type words into my laptop and
in the same second exactly the same words can be heard on TV
or radio.» 46) Sabine Mayhofer · Organization Consultant ·
4.12.66 · Zaubertal/Austria · «Experiencing the moment when
people find their answers.» 47) Matthew Sleeth · Photographer ·
7.9.72 · Melbourne/Australia · «Not sure.»

Back Issues

---   –

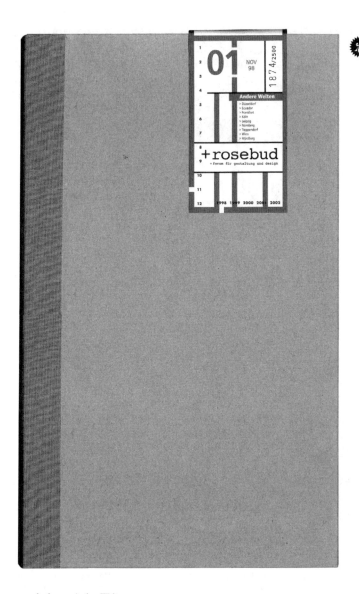

+rosebud no.1 – Andere Welten
Strictly limited and numbered edition, full color, 195 x 300 mm, 112 pages, hardcover, perfect binding, sealed cover, set of postcards. Awarded with an Art Directors Club Germany Award. **Sold Out!**

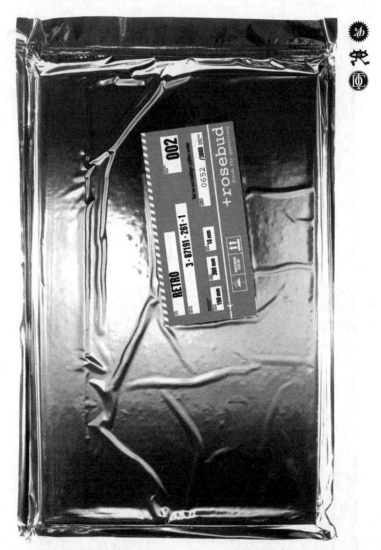

+rosebud no.2 – RETRO
Strictly limited and numbered edition, full color, 195 x 300 mm, 112 pages, hardcover, perfect binding, embossed cover wrapped in alminum foil, incl. mini RETRO-encyclopedia, stickerpage, set of postcards. Awarded with a Bronze Medal from the Art Directors Club Germany, «High Design Quality» from the German Prize for Communication Design and the Certificate of Typographic Excellence from the Type Directors Club New York/TDC 46. **Sold out!**

ADC'E

Das ist der Text für ein Buchcover. Vorerst steht hier noch ein beliebiger und nichtssagender Text. Ein Text der in der richtigen grafischen Aufbereitung ausschliesslich dazu dient, den Titel dieses Buches aussagekräftig zu machen. Selbstverständlich ist die hier abgebildete Zeichenkette nur dazu geeignet, einen allgemeinen visuellen Eindruck zu vermitteln. Der tatsächliche Inhalt ist in diesem Moment noch völlig nebensächlich. Der Betrachter soll den Text ja gar nicht lesen um nicht von der äusseren Form abgelenkt zu werden. Dieser Text wird in dieser Form natürlich nie in Druck gehen. Später wird er allerdings sehr ausführlich über das Thema und die Inhalte dieses Buches informieren. Vorerst kommt ihm jedoch nur eine reine Platzhalterfunktion zu, obgleich Schriftart, Schriftgrösse, Zeilenabstand und Laufweite bereits einen verbindlichen Eindruck über das Erscheinungsbild vermitteln sollen. Nur so kann das Cover unter rein formalen Gesichtspunkten objektiv beurteilt werden. Dies ist insbesondere bei einem Designbuch von großer Bedeutung, da hier der Gestaltung des Titels eine wichtige Rolle bei der Kaufentscheidung zukommt. This text is for the cover of a book. At the moment, it is just random meaningless text. It is text that serves to emphasize the title of this publication by being placed in its formal graphical context. Of course the chain of symbols depicted here is only employed to convey a visual impression. The actual contents are totally irrelevant at the moment. The reader isn't even supposed to read the text to insure that it doesn't distract him from the form. Of course this text will never go into print in this version. However, later it will offer

"One of the most arresting, insightful and scandalous books in recent memory…"
MARKETING MANAGER

"A publishing milestone."
PRODUCTION COORDINATOR

"This is the book I wish I had written."
INTERN

"The one book on Blindtext I'd have if I could have just one. A classic."
EDITOR-IN-CHIEF

+rosebud no.3 – Blindtext
Strictly limited and numbered edition, full color, 170 x 245 mm, 200 pages, bilingual, hardcover, perfect binding, incl. exclusive micro-novel «The Lost Mind» by Joseph von Westphalen. Awarded with a Silver Medal from the Art Directors Club Germany, «High Design Quality» from the Red-Dot Design Award, «One of Germany's Most Beautiful Books 2001» from the German Buchkunst Foundation, the Certificate of Typographic Excellence from the Type Directors Club New York / TDC 48 and was also nominated for the Art Directors Club of Europe (ADCE) Awards. Available in bookstores worldwide or through www.amazon.com & www.amazon.de,
ISBN: 3-931126-54-4

+rosebud no.4 – ACTION
Strictly limited and numbered edition, four different covers, full color, 250 x 260 mm, 208 pages, bilingual, perfect binding, incl. flip-book, interactive poster and stickerpage. Awarded with a Gold Medal from the Art Directors Club Germany, a Golden Venus from the Creative Club Austria and was also nominated for the Art Directors Club of Europe (ADCE) Awards. **Available in bookstores worldwide or through www.amazon.com & www.amazon.de, ISBN: 3-931126-98-6**

Mystery — An Absurd Chapter in Book History

---   -

Based on an Idea by Erich Pöttschacher

Debut Performance on January 31, 2004 in Vienna

---   -

Introduction

In the early afternoon of January 31, 2004, nine men and six women meet in an entirely empty room at the office premises of Rosebud, Inc. On the floor a rectangle has been accurately marked out by four strips of adhesive tape. None of the persons present appears to have even the faintest idea concerning the object of the meeting. What exactly developed among the people present in the room during the following minutes, has remained an absolute mystery to outside observers until the present day. In a peculiar way the scene obviously represents the real encounter of nine selected chapters of a book entitled «Mystery.»

This is their true story.

The Cast

Kristina Gilmer .... ROSEMARY BROWN *

Catharina Roland .... HAUFF

Erwin Bauer .... MONSTER WATER

Yudi Warsosumarto .... SOFIE'S WORLD

Birgit Vollmeier .... HYPNOSIS **

Claire Schillinger .... BRUNNSTEINER

Christoph Brunmayr .... RECEIPTS ***

Peter Suk .... ROSEBUD, AUSTRALIA

Elisabeth Stögmann .... CHAIRS

Directed by .... Sabine Mayhofer

Assistance .... Susumo Ono

*   sic. «Voices from the Beyond»
**   contribution not realized
***   sic. «Proof of Purchase»

NOTE

Structural constellations are based on the principle
(as yet lacking a detailed scientific explanation)
that systemic behaviour can be reconstructed phenome-
nologically by putting each of the relevant elements
of the system in a specific—physical—place. A system
in this context may be a family as well as an organization, a team or a script. From the perspective of a
constellation, individual behaviour can only be described in terms of the relationship and communication
with other elements of the system.

The physical positioning of persons in a room therefore permits the representation of complex social
systems, whereby the representatives participating in
the constellation may take on the part of real persons
(e.g. members of the family, employees, colleagues)
but also of abstract meaningful units (e.g. a symptom,
a fictitious movie character, a target).

For Mystery, various chapters characteristic of the
book's content and process of creation were selected
and represented in a so-called «pars party» and
«mythical play» constellation. The participants of the
constellation had been given only minimal information
on the part of the book represented by them and were
then left to act freely in the room. The unabridged
protocol describes what happened over a period of approximately 90 minutes.

Thus, Mystery is probably the first book ever whose
pages have communicated with each other.

A bleak, unfurnished office.
One after another, people enter through a door, coming to a standstill inside a rectangular area marked on the floor.

As it has been defined beforehand, everyone states its current feeling:

SOFIE'S WORLD: (carries a flower-pot with an Aloe Vera plant)
«Love, romance, treat me tenderly once I'm inside.»

ROSEMARY BROWN: «Quite harmonious, a little sad, but bright.»

ROSEBUD, AUSTRALIA: «A city, a haunted city.»

RECEIPTS: «I feel great, I like all that.»

BRUNNSTEINER (Carries a cookie jar, a golden Venus figurine, crayons, scotch tape and some sheets of paper): «Must withdraw, was bored. Sad and glad, to have so many things with me.»

MONSTER WATER (coming from the bathroom): «I could actually be anywhere.»

HAUFF : «Agressions, I feel a little agressive, I would like to clout ROSEMARY BROWN.»

HYPNOSIS : «Empty, alone, but different and new.»

CHAIRS : «From far away, strong, important, a little isolated, but important.»

From that moment, like automatically, a soundless scene unfolds.
During the following procedures nobody says a single word.

BRUNNSTEINER appears to be anxious, bored, starts to snicker. Places the sheets of paper on the floor and distributes crayons. CHAIRS pushes the crayons aside.

SOFIE'S WORLD places a plant in front of BRUNNSTEINER.

HAUFF tears up BRUNNSTEINER's papers and withdraws into a corner.

RECEIPTS wants to take away the plant, BRUNNSTEINER fends her off.

BRUNNSTEINER takes plant along to SOFIE'S WORLD.

ROSEMARY BROWN snuggles up to BRUNNSTEINER, SOFIE'S WORLD joins in. HAUFF beats up on BRUNNSTEINER.

CHAIRS chooses another corner.

SOFIE'S WORLD confronts HAUFF, carries plant to RECEIPTS and holds a sheet of paper in front of her eyes.

RECEIPTS sticks a shred of paper on the plant.

CHAIRS appears to be bored, isolated, sits splay-legged on the floor, slightly obscene.

BRUNNSTEINER paints in front of MONSTER WATER, ROSEBUD, AUS-TRALIA joins in.

BRUNNSTEINER attacks HAUFF, sits down beside ROSEMARY BROWN, MONSTER WATER sits down between BRUNNSTEINER and ROSEMARY BROWN.

BRUNNSTEINER paints HYPNOSIS, tears up the sheets of paper and tosses the shreds into the crowd. HAUFF snatches at the paper.

SOFIE'S WORLD sits down next to CHAIRS.

BRUNNSTEINER throws paper shreds at RECEIPTS.

HAUFF blocks BRUNNSTEINER's way, BRUNNSTEINER runs around, thumps ROSEMARY BROWN, makes a noise, laughs.

SOFIE'S WORLD moves away from CHAIRS, steps up to HYPNOSIS.

HAUFF annoyed, follows BRUNNSTEINER, SOFIE'S WORLD stands between them.

BRUNNSTEINER shows cookies, but doesn't share, plays around with SOFIE'S WORLD, SOFIE'S WORLD gets a cookie, BRUNNSTEINER is still laughing.

SOFIE'S WORLD shares cookies with ROSEMARY BROWN.

CHAIRS bored, sitting on the floor, MONSTER WATER joins her.

BRUNNSTEINER distributes cookies.

HAUFF arms widespread, stands in the middle of the room, ROSEBUD, AUSTRALIA watches.

BRUNNSTEINER still distributing cookies to CHAIRS and MONSTER WATER.

SOFIE'S WORLD decorates the plant, adorns herself.

BRUNNSTEINER grabs Venus and places her in a corner.

RECEIPTS is restless.

MONSTER WATER exchanges a picture for a plant, goes back to CHAIRS.

BRUNNSTEINER paints feet on paper.

HYPNOSIS still standing at the edge of the field—calm, lost.

BRUNNSTEINER active, loud—whistles, takes ROSEMARY BROWN's papers away, HAUFF intercedes.

SOFIE'S WORLD wants to give a slip of paper to HYPNOSIS, no reaction, others accept papers.

CHAIRS absent.

RECEIPTS still in the corner.

BRUNNSTEINER places crayons in the form of a circle, HAUFF steps into the circle and stands back-to-back with BRUNNSTEINER.

SOFIE'S WORLD destroys the circle, HAUFF and BRUNNSTEINER put everything back together.

SOFIE'S WORLD burrows into her blanket, inside the circle BRUNNSTEINER plays around with HAUFF, ROSEBUD, AUSTRALIA enters the circle.

HYPNOSIS turns in a semicircle and gazes at the scene in front of her.

BRUNNSTEINER decorates HAUFF, ROSEBUD, AUSTRALIA leaves the circle and walks over to HYPNOSIS.

BRUNNSTEINER walks around HAUFF, claps, stands in the center.

RECEIPTS nervous, embarrassed.

ROSEMARY BROWN stands up, grabs a jacket, sits down again; BRUNNSTEINER claps, sings, thumps cookie jar.

SOFIE'S WORLD crawls away with a plant, BRUNNSTEINER consoles her and offers crayons to HAUFF; HAUFF declines and turns around in a circle.

CHAIRS yawns, lies down.

RECEIPTS increasingly nervous.

BRUNNSTEINER places cookie dishes around HAUFF, SOFIE'S WORLD adds paper.

ROSEBUD, AUSTRALIA sits down back-to-back with ROSEMARY BROWN and BRUNNSTEINER.

SOFIE'S WORLD ducks down, runs to RECEIPTS, crouches down on her knees and crawls over to the group.

HAUFF still standing inside the circle.

HYPNOSIS and HAUFF approch each other.

CHAIRS takes BRUNNSTEINER in her arms.

HAUFF leads HYPNOSIS into the room; irritated, RECEIPTS confronts BRUNNSTEINER.

SOFIE'S WORLD gives a jacket to HYPNOSIS, BRUNNSTEINER takes it
away from her, HAUFF fetches back the jacket.

SOFIE'S WORLD runs along the edge of the field, BRUNNSTEINER sticks
scotch tape on everybody, MONSTER WATER sits down back-to-back with
ROSEMARY BROWN and ROSEBUD, AUSTRALIA.

SOFIE'S WORLD jumps up and down, dances around the others, HAUFF
stands inside a painted circle, BRUNNSTEINER again in the middle.

CHAIRS and BRUNNSTEINER laugh.

SOFIE'S WORLD extroverted, theatric.

HAUFF shivers, starts tap-dancing, turns in a circle; BRUNNSTEINER takes
HYPNOSIS by the arm and turns around, so she is standing in front of
HAUFF.

BRUNNSTEINER leads HAUFF to the other side.

ROSEBUD, AUSTRALIA stands in the center, BRUNNSTEINER still
leads HAUFF around, banters with SOFIE'S WORLD, aggravates HAUFF,
alternately offering and withdrawing crayons.

ROSEBUD, AUSTRALIA standing with HAUFF in the center of the circle.

BRUNNSTEINER strolls around with SOFIE'S WORLD, annoys HAUFF;
HAUFF gets angry, fetches Venus, walks back into the circle.

BRUNNSTEINER flirts, banters with SOFIE'S WORLD; now SOFIE'S
WORLD is also standing inside the circle.

CHAIRS yawns absently.

SOFIE'S WORLD and BRUNNSTEINER joke with everybody, hand out slips
of paper.

BRUNNSTEINER gives a piece of his identification to HYPNOSIS.

HYPNOSIS hands out her own papers to BRUNNSTEINER,
BRUNNSTEINER drops the papers on the floor.

SOFIE'S WORLD spreads her arms, «flies» around.

BRUNNSTEINER provokes RECEIPTS.

SOFIE'S WORLD pratises push-ups, BRUNNSTEINER pushes down on
SOFIE'S WORLD and finally sits on SOFIE'S WORLD's back.

HAUFF holds Venus and watches.

SOFIE'S WORLD jumps around, plays around with HAUFF and crayons.

ROSEMARY BROWN sits with eyes half closed.

BRUNNSTEINER and SOFIE'S WORLD affected, walk around HAUFF
clapping, HAUFF stands up in a winners pose, holds up venus.

BRUNNSTEINER wants to take Venus away, HAUFF holds on tight, doesn't
back down.

MONSTER WATER pulls at HAUFF's skirt, HAUFF shows no reaction.

HAUFF still standing in the center holding up Venus.

MONSTER WATER stands up, moves on to another corner.

ROSEMARY BROWN lies down next to BRUNNSTEINER.

CHAIRS uses paper to build models of chairs together with ROSEBUD, AUS-
TRALIA.

RECEIPTS gets a cigarette from outside, MONSTER WATER walks around.

HYPNOSIS snatches Venus, doesn't return her in spite of HAUFF's requests,
HAUFF holds up crayons instead.

SOFIE'S WORLD sets down the plant in front of HAUFF.

HYPNOSIS collects objects, places them in packets in the corners of the field.

ROSEMARY BROWN lies motionless on the floor.

BRUNNSTEINER and SOFIE'S WORLD noisy and restless, provoking
HAUFF, BRUNNSTEINER steals Venus from HAUFF.

ROSEBUD, AUSTRALIA stands up, stops next to CHAIRS.

HAUFF runs after BRUNNSTEINER, wants Venus back, clutches SOFIE'S WORLD, grabs Venus and holds her up in a winners pose; BRUNNSTEINER applauds, drums, also SOFIE'S WORLD drums and hands out cookies.

ROSEMARY BROWN accepts cookies.

BRUNNSTEINER and SOFIE'S WORLD very egocentric, exalted, stage their own play on the stage.

It seems that finally everybody found his/her place; only SOFIE'S WORLD and BRUNNSTEINER walk around.

CHAIRS stirs, but in the end sits down again.

HAUFF again builds a circle in the center.

BRUNNSTEINER and SOFIE'S WORLD stand bantering at the edge of the field.

HYPNOSIS again places objects in the corners, puts everything in order.

HAUFF standing in a winners pose in the center, doesn't get a lot of attention.

ROSEMARY BROWN sleeping in the meantime.

BRUNNSTEINER loudly yawning.

ROSEBUD, AUSTRALIA and MONSTER WATER stand together.

BRUNNSTEINER walks around HAUFF, annoys HAUFF, sings to HAUFF, SOFIE'S WORLD examines both, HAUFF pushes BRUNNSTEINER and SOFIE'S WORLD out of the circle.

CHAIRS claims paper modell back from BRUNNSTEINER.

HYPNOSIS destroys the circle, HAUFF opposes.

HAUFF rebuilds the circle, Venus is standing in the center.

HAUFF places Venus on top of his own pictures, SOFIE'S WORLD again decorates the plant.

BRUNNSTEINER covers ROSEMARY BROWN with a jacket, at the same time disrupts her by thumping the cookie jar.

is mixed with associations and   454

MONSTER WATER sticks his own picture on BRUNNSTEINER,
BRUNNSTEINER wants more.

BRUNNSTEINER takes a slip of paper away from HAUFF, HAUFF follows
BRUNNSTEINER, wants his bounty back, succeeds.

BRUNNSTEINER gives HAUFF a picture from MONSTER WATER, but
HAUFF places the picture on the floor.

CHAIRS still lying splay-legged on the floor.

SOFIE'S WORLD and BRUNNSTEINER play pantomime, make noises to
provoke RECEIPTS, RECEIPTS keeps cool.

SOFIE'S WORLD and BRUNNSTEINER fool around, disguise themselves,
act lasciviously towards HAUFF.

SOFIE'S WORLD carries Venus back into the field, HYPNOSIS immediately
places Venus oustide the field again.

Everyone is sitting, only BRUNNSTEINER, SOFIE'S WORLD, RECEIPTS,
and HAUFF are still standing.

HAUFF sits down.

SOFIE'S WORLD sits down.

BRUNNSTEINER sits with ROSEMARY BROWN, lies down on her.

RECEIPTS is the last one standing.

BRUNNSTEINER disturbes ROSEMARY BROWN, stands up again, sits down
with drums.

MONSTER WATER stands up.

ROSEMARY BROWN rebuffs BRUNNSTEINER, sits up.

RECEIPTS and MONSTER WATER standing in a corner.

SOFIE'S WORLD and BRUNNSTEINER stand together.

MONSTER WATER runs along the edge.

BRUNNSTEINER histrionic, daft, sweeps SOFIE'S WORLD along.

HAUFF stands up, BRUNNSTEINER disrupts, provokes.

HAUFF walks back into the circle, SOFIE'S WORLD follows with a plant.

HAUFF leans over to SOFIE'S WORLD.

MONSTER WATER, RECEIPTS, and ROSEBUD, AUSTRALIA stand together.

BRUNNSTEINER lets everybody stick things on his body.

HAUFF sleeping on SOFIE'S WORLD's shoulder, HYPNOSIS gives out a picture, sticks it on the plant.

BRUNNSTEINER sits down with SOFIE'S WORLD, HAUFF, and ROSEMARY BROWN, MONSTER WATER join them.

CHAIRS and ROSEBUD, AUSTRALIA lean on BRUNNSTEINER.

RECEIPTS still standing, is invited to join the group, declines.

HAUFF takes MONSTER WATER and SOFIE'S WORLD in his arms.

BRUNNSTEINER stands in the center of the group.

BRUNNSTEINER impatient, ROSEBUD, AUSTRALIA stands up, moves away from the crowd, BRUNNSTEINER asks ROSEBUD, AUSTRALIA back, ROSEBUD, AUSTRALIA returns to the group.

BRUNNSTEINER walks over to a corner, wants to take Venus and ROSEMARY BROWN with him, ROSEMARY BROWN declines.

CHAIRS, ROSEBUD, AUSTRALIA, and MONSTER WATER walk over to BRUNNSTEINER.

SOFIE'S WORLD with a little distance, ROSEBUD, AUSTRALIA and MONSTER WATER walk around SOFIE'S WORLD.

ROSEMARY BROWN now is alone.

BRUNNSTEINER stands in the center, the others are sitting, HAUFF and RECEIPTS stand in a corner, HYPNOSIS at the edge.

CHAIRS again sitting in a casual pose.

BRUNNSTEINER walks to RECEIPTS and HAUFF.

HAUFF holds up Venus, BRUNNSTEINER places the plant into the center.

HAUFF slides Venus over to RECEIPTS, BRUNNSTEINER retrieves Venus, again HAUFF takes her away, BRUNNSTEINER follows.

The End.

Rosebud, Australia

---   -

by Matthew Sleeth

---   -

```
To:         ask@rosebudmagazine.com
Subject:    Pictures from Australia
Date:       July 12, 2003  15:10:46  GMT+02:00
```

Hi Ralf,

I have just come across your magazine on the internet
and thought you might be interested in a project I
am working on. The attached pictures are from ROSEBUD,
a small seaside town (about an hour from Melbourne,
Australia) which is a very popular summer holiday
destination. It is also very rundown and tacky.

I hope they are of interest.

Cheers,
Matthew

between the US and Australia.

466

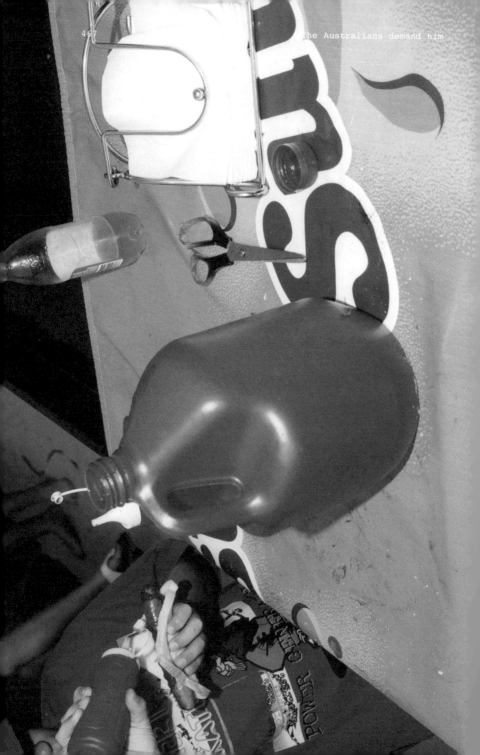

The Australians demand him

OFFICE

ROSEBUD
CAR RENTALS

Clean, Reliable Automatics

from $2? Per Day

5982 2070

470

+rosebud no.6

PUBLIC
BRIEFING

Wed, September 4, 2004
20:00 (CET)

BROADCAST LIVE ON:
www.rosebudmagazine.com

At night, when it got quiet outside
light broke through the crack and left me with an afterglow.